Science, Art, and Communication

Science, Art, and Communication

by John R. Pierce

 Clarkson N. Potter, Inc./Publisher NEW YORK

"Don't Write, Telegraph," "Chance Remarks," "Science for Art's Sake," and "Washington Dateline," reprinted by permission of John R. Pierce from *Astounding Science Fiction* (now *Analog Science Fiction–Science Fact*); copyright © 1949, 1950, 1952, by Street & Smith Publications, Inc.

"Orbital Radio Relays," reprinted with permission from *Jet Propulsion*, April, 1955; copyright © 1955, by the American Rocket Society, Inc.

"Transoceanic Communication by Means of Satellites," reprinted with permission from a paper published in *The Proceedings of the Institute of Radio Engineers*, March, 1959. Copyright © 1959, by the Institute of Radio Engineers, Inc.

"International Communication and Space," originally prepared for broadcast by the Voice of America in a series of *Forum* lectures on "Space Science." Reprinted with permission.

"Satellite Science and Technology," reprinted by permission of John R. Pierce from *Science,* Vol. 141, No. 3577 (July 19, 1963), 237–244; copyright © 1963, by the American Association for the Advancement of Science.

"Freedom in Research," reprinted by permission of John R. Pierce from *Science,* Vol. 130 (September 4, 1959), 540–542.

"The Social Uses of Science," reprinted with permission from *American Scientist,* Vol. 42, No. 4 (October, 1954), 646-650; copyright © 1954, by the Society of Sigma Xi.

"Planning and Readiness," reprinted with permission from "Forecasting the Future," *Science Journal,* Vol. 3, No. 10 (October, 1967), 76–81.

"Portrait of the Machine as a Young Artist" originally appeared in *Playboy* magazine; copyright © 1965, by HMH Publishing Co., Inc. Reprinted with permission.

"Computer Synthesis of Musical Sounds," reprinted from *The Rockefeller University Review,* November, 1965, with the permission of The Rockefeller University Press; copyright © 1966, by the Rockefeller University Press.

"Artists and Machines," reprinted with permission from the Catalog of "Bewogen Beweging," Stedelijk Museum, Amsterdam, March 10–April 17, 1961.

"Science, Technology, and Art," from a lecture delivered at "Fylkingen," Visions of the Present, Stockholm, September, 1961, and published in the *Fylkingen International Bulletin,* Vol. 1 (1967). Reprinted with permission.

To Clarkson N. Potter,
who first asked me
to write a book

Preface: In Praise of Ignorance

THE world is so full of people, and things, of societies and nations, arts, crafts, books and sciences, that anyone can remain ignorant, no matter how much he learns. Indeed, knowledge can open our eyes to new vistas of ignorance.

No one understands this better than the scientist or the engineer. The things that seem most challenging and important to us are the things that we don't understand. It is the spur of ignorance, the consciousness of not understanding and the curiosity about that which lies beyond, that are essential to the progress of science and technology.

The knowledge, craft, and worldly wisdom we acquire enable us to solve old problems and tackle new ones. But without a consciousness of ignorance, scientists and engineers would be dead.

A superficial knowledge of government, business, and the arts, scraped off through intimate though very limited contact rather than learned from books, has convinced me that ignorance is universal.

Men in Washington know a great deal that other people don't know, including how to get elected or to hold down administrative jobs. They exercise skill and considerable worldly wisdom in dealing with a host of pressing problems. But it would be absurd to think that they understand the extremely complicated structure and function of our society anymore than we really understand the functioning of our internal organs. And, they can do no more than make informed guesses as to where the country is heading, even as we can only make informed guesses as to our individual futures.

Men in business are also skilled and knowledgeable, but their skill and knowledge are limited, and they too are beset by a host of forces which are beyond both their control and their comprehension. Artists and scholars amaze me with their special skills and knowledge, but the skills are special and the knowledge is not final.

Knowledge can open our eyes. The scientist, the engineer, the

7

politician or civil servant, the businessman, the artist each sees in the behavior of nature, men, or organizations something that the less informed miss, and with skill, each can manipulate or make use of what he sees. Knowledge sharpens our vision. Skill makes us effective. But it is a consciousness of ignorance that can keep us alive.

Without ignorance we cannot learn. When ignorance vanishes, we fall prey to final wisdom; we know beyond doubt what is right, what is wrong, what is good, what is bad, where the world and the country are headed, where they should be headed. At best we become as limited as Jowett is said to have been.[1] At worst we become hardened against man as well as against knowledge, willing to cause monumental suffering to achieve ends which we regard as unassailable.

The pieces in this book reflect the writer's exposure over several decades to various areas of human activity and human knowledge. Differences in style and tone reflect differences in time, problem, reaction, and audience. The book will certainly not dispel the reader's ignorance. I hope it may enlarge his sense of what he doesn't know and doesn't understand—that is, broaden his ignorance. Indeed, it might even help to jar him out of certitude, as I am jarred from time to time, and will continue to be jarred as long as I am really alive.

NOTES

[1] My name is Benjamin Jowett
And what there is to know, I know it.
I am the Master of Balliol College
And what I do not know is not knowledge.[2]

—Author unknown

[2] This reminds me of some newspapers.

Contents

I Up in the Air

II Way Out

III Science, Scientists, and Society

IV But Is It Art?

Author's Note

The pieces in this book were originally published elsewhere or delivered as lectures. Some were intended for a technical audience, and were full of equations; others overlapped considerably. In adapting them for this book, I have deleted technical, mathematical, and repetitious material, and have added only footnotes.

11

Abbreviations Used in This Book

ac—alternating current

B.E.M.—bug-eyed monster

cm—centimeter

dB—decibel ($10 \log_{10} [P_2/P_1]$, where P_1 and P_2 are two powers)

dBw—decibel referred to one watt ($10 \log_{10} P$, where P is power in watts

FM—frequency modulation

IF—intermediate frequency

kMc—kilomegacycles (thousands of megacycles)

kW—kilowatt

mw—milliwatt

Mc—megacycle (a million alternations a second)

Mw—megawatt

MeV—megaelectron volt (energy of an electron accelerated by a million volts)

nmi—nautical mile

PCM—pulse-code modulation

p-n—A p-n junction is a rectifying junction in a semi-conductor; on the p side, current is carried by positive "holes," and on the n side, by electrons.

®—Registered Service Mark

RF—radio frequency

I
Up In The Air

The Wings of the Wind

IT seems to me that in our age of space and war, danger costs a great deal and people take it very seriously. When I was young, neither the press nor movements paid much attention when five fellow enthusiasts were killed flying homemade gliders. Danger didn't bother me when I didn't feel that it was there. My recollections are happy or amused. When I look out over a valley, or when someone mentions *Point Counterpoint,* or if someone says "the lone hawk" (which I hear repeated as "the lone hork"), I think of gliding. Other things remind me.

The Treaty of Versailles forbade Germany to build powered aircraft, and German gliding was born. That is not my story. My story begins when I read in the *National Geographic Magazine* a wonderful article, "On the Wings of the Wind." What teenager would not thrill to the pictures of beautiful and strangely shaped sailplanes soaring over romantic German countrysides? How romantic, too, were the foreign names: the universities of Aachen and Darmstadt, where the students had formed clubs to build and fly gliders; the name of the carpenter, Espenlaub, and the pictures of his progressively sleeker machines; the Schopskopf, the hill over which they sailed. How much I would have given to have flown for hours and to have covered tens and hundreds of miles, as the pilot Schultz had done!

THE THREE OF US

Perhaps all, instead of most, of this would have remained a romantic fancy had there not been other crazy boys at Woodrow Wilson High School in Long Beach, California, in 1927. But there was Oliver La Rue, and there was Apollo Smith, who is now an aerodyn-

15

amicist with Douglas Aircraft. Perhaps Apollo was the chief ingredient, for it was at his house that we built the glider. Apollo had a more technical background than either Oliver or I. His father, Orsino, who was a chemical engineer, followed closely what we did. Apollo's sisters, Diana and Athena, and his brother Hermes were interested onlookers.

The glider which we built in Apollo's garage was conceived in ignorance and begot of bicycle spokes for turnbuckles, wagon wheels, piano wire, and fancy. The airfoil was laid out by Oliver La Rue with freehand sweeps. At a moderate pace, the rickety monstrosity grew. Finally we wheeled it to the top of an inadequate hill close at hand and collected a crowd willing to pull a rope. Apollo got into the seat, and we and the rest ran down the hill against the wind. The glider picked up speed. Then one wing rose. When the glider fell, it seemed to be a mass of broken sticks. But only the too-fragile struts holding the wing were broken, and these we soon replaced.

THE LONG BEACH GLIDER CLUB

About the time of our fiasco we found that we were not the only people in California who were interested in gliding. There was a glider club in Long Beach. Every Sunday the members met at Crawford's Airport and flew their gliders from the level ground. A good number came out to fly and see, and they were needed. In those days gliders took off by means of a huge slingshot of rubber rope called shock cord. This rope was formed into a vee, and a ring at the apex caught a hook at the glider's nose. Two groups ran forward with the free ends of the shock cord, while a man held the glider back as long as he could. When he let go, the glider rushed forward on its skid, took to the air, and flew a few hundred feet.

It was good that the gliders didn't go farther, for those who first took them up had never been in the air before. Ed Gettins worked in a refinery. He had patterned his ship after pictures in N.A.C.A.[1] material obtained through his congressman. Ray Chesley and Jimmy Caruso were high school students like us, but they were better informed and more skilled woodworkers. They had built a beautiful orange training ship, weak only in that they had hollowed out the members which joined the wings to the landing skid. These tended to shatter.

Frank Slaughter was a sign painter who then had no glider of his own, but he showed us pictures of a weird device he had copied from an early German article.

FRANK SLAUGHTER

Gliding in Southern California was born of a highly developed German art, but it grew in a peculiar way. In those first days it was practiced, not by wealthy men or sportsmen, not by those who knew something of aviation, but by the ignorant, the odd, the impecunious. Those who had a romantic turn and plenty of time and could scrape together a hundred dollars or so built gliders. Frank Slaughter was an example. He was a sign painter, and a good one. Over wood he could put a simulated marble which deceived at arm's length, and was handsome as well, however unsuited it was to the counters of his kitchenette. There weren't many signs or counters to paint just then. Some of his leisure he used in painting in a pointillistic manner bright California landscapes on sections sawed from logs. Partly, he took photographs with a huge old Graphlex, and then ruined the negatives by developing them in Long Beach water, which ate the emulsion into little shreds. His greatest love, however—or was that his young and pretty wife?—was gliding.

At the dawn of that gliding era, Frank had built what must by its very nature have been a sailplane. It consisted chiefly of a long horizontal boom fastened to a fore-and-aft member. Between these were stretched—canvas sails! Overhead flew two small jibs with handles to be grasped by the pilot, and with these one was to control the beast.

Clear to the top of the Palos Verdes Hills, a thousand feet above the sea, he had carted this contraption, rehearsing the flight-to-be in the movements of his decrepit car. The monster refused to take off. When he returned in a high wind, he was able to fly in it kitewise, and whipped back and forth wildly at the end of a rope. He dared no farther in this aerial windjammer.

When we first knew him, Frank was gliderless but full of plans. He had painted a handsome picture of his dream ship in glowing colors, and bit by bit he was building it in his garage. Was the spar too heavy? He sawed out most of the plywood web, although he could easily have flown with the pieces he removed in his pockets. Was the spar now too weak? He dipped the ends of sticks in glue and wedged them into the apertures from which he had removed the plywood. In the happiest of ignorance, he provided thin tension members across one diagonal of a bay of the fuselage, and nothing across the other. Month on month, he lived in anticipation of the day when his sailplane would be finished. Meanwhile, the club bought a huge golden training glider which some enthusiast had built, and we all learned to fly.

MAC

Frank Slaughter wasn't the only painter in the Long Beach Glider Club; there was Mac. Today I don't remember his last name.

Mac was a small, dark, wiry-moustached man who kept a show-windowed shop cluttered with glider, although the tools of his trade and a few *tours de force* hung on the walls. I particularly remember a pair of partially draped women who held golden trays vertically on their shoulders.

Mac differed a little from the other glider enthusiasts. For one thing, I believe that he had even less money. When he appeared at a glider meet, all politeness to the lady who accompanied him, the starch of his cuffs could not hide their tatters. And, Mac was an inventor. Other enthusiasts built their bric-a-brac of fancy on solid Teutonic foundations. Mac's glider had feathers. Too, the wing was upside down.

While stodgy scientists were misled by their unnatural wind tunnels, Mac watched the birds and reasoned. Something must keep those turkey buzzards up there for hours on end. What did they have that airplanes lacked? Feathers! So, Mac had built a model—or he said he had done so—with a long cross spar, wires to the tips, canvas vanes (feathers) stretched fore and aft, and a sail-like sheath above. It flew, he claimed, away and away. In proof of this, he didn't have the model anymore.

Now he was working on the real thing. Because he was so poor, instead of the steel and plywood he needed, he had for his spar only a wood frame over which he stretched craft paper wet, varnishing the taut surface when it dried. The spar was braced with piano wire which he stretched by means of the worm keys from old mandolins. How could a man accomplish anything under such handicaps?

His convinced or convincing words must have fallen on sympathetic ears, for metal-working tools appeared suddenly in his shop, together with tanks of oxygen and acetylene.

Slowly, his great bird took form. Carefully, he bent the mild steel into light angle irons, and he brazed these painstakingly together. Then, with a hand punch, he removed countless quarter-inch disks of negligible weight, to lighten the structure.

Mac was always ready to stop and explain his automatic control system, in which a weighted stick hung from above and swung so as to correct the motion of the craft. It didn't matter, of course, that the pilot had to move the stick opposite from the way he would in other gliders.

Handicapped by lack of funds and by friendly conversation, it took Mac a long time to build his ever-flying bird. During the many months, he had his shop, and he ate—I wonder at whose expense?

This could not go on forever. There came a day when the machine was finished. I wish I knew what really happened then. All that I could learn was that the bird had been spirited off to the Palos Verdes Hills in the cold gray of a morning, with Frank Slaughter along as pilot. I imagine that the backer was there as well. Thenceforth, I saw no more and heard no more of the bird. Mac lost his shop, and when I met him again he had become a convert of *The Book,* a disciple of Coin Harvey, more interested in politics and economics than in gliding.

MR. KLEWIE

Mr. Klewie was a tall, strongly built, dignified man with a German accent. He always carried books about. I saw him once with Aldous Huxley's *Point Counterpoint.* That strange title stuck with me for years, until finally I read the book. Mr. Klewie did not have a glider. When, sometimes accompanied by his modest wife, he came around to see how we were getting on, he showed us letters and pamphlets from friends in Germany. He talked about the glider plans they would send him.

It was too bad that Mr. Klewie had so little leisure to devote to the sport of gliding. His profession, his wife informed my mother, took most of his time. What was his profession? my mother asked. Mr. Klewie was a stevedore.

GLIDER MEET

Gradually, the members of the Long Beach Glider Club learned to fly without disaster. They became discontented with the safe but feeble rubber catapult, and were towed across the airport behind a car at the end of hundreds of feet of rope. Attaining dizzy heights, they could make slipping turns and other ill-conceived maneuvers. Apollo took our glider to the top of the Palos Verdes Hills and stalled on takeoff, completely shattering the triangular fuselage. We built a better one in the form of the guyed flat lattice of the German training ship. We flew better poised on the skid that jutted out ahead of all else. Aloft so, we could see nothing but our feet and the scene below. We had a sense of truly flying, and boundless ambition for more. Clearly, we were ready for a glider meet.

The meet was held a hundred miles away, in San Diego. We put the wings of our glider on the roof of the Packard, the fuselage on a trailer behind, and off we went. When we had arrived at the top of the hill and assembled our glider, we took off toward the plain below and flew over a real live news cameraman, wondering whether or not we would clear him.

There, too, we met Hawley Bowlus, who had hung over the cliffs ten hours or more to set the American endurance record, the man first in our country to surpass the record that the Wright Brothers had set so many years ago. Bowlus' ships were nothing compared with German sailplanes, and there was something of the publicist in him. To us, however, his gliders were marvels and he was envied jealously as a man of great accomplishments.

I was rattled at the meet and flew badly; I did get the spot landing cup, for landing nearest a mark. But Apollo and our ship flew like marvels. He won so many cups that I think it was only through local prejudice that Bowlus was judged to be winner of the meet.

There was something wonderful about our glider which was missing in copies. Apollo and I have wondered what it could have been. It was of no use to copy the shapes of the ribs of the wings, for they were far apart and the cloth sagged between them, touching the spars. In some way, we had hit by accident on a most suitable wing profile, and the glider flew like a charm.

I WRITE A BOOK

Between high school and Caltech (California Institute of Technology) I was full of knowledge. In this state I was approached by Hugo Gernsback, that Great Cham of amateur tinkering, the founder in an earlier day of the Electro-Importing Company, the publisher of *The Electrical Experimenter*, the first editor of *Science and Invention*, the father of science fiction who created *Amazing Stories*. This Hugo Gernsback asked me to write a book about gliding, to be brought out in magazine style for a dollar, uniform with *Strictly Private* or *Should the Doctor Tell?* by Maurice Chideckel, M.D. Was I likely to refuse?

Producing a book was something else. I did account for 40 pages out of the total of 93. The rest was pieced out with material from N.A.C.A. reports, probably taking no heed of copyrights. Thus, in 1929: *How to Build and Fly Gliders*.

I have often wondered whether this book, together with other articles I wrote for Gernsback's magazines, did real harm. Certainly people read them and took them seriously, for people wrote me asking for plans. I even got a letter from Australia asking whether an enclosed sample of wood was suitable for a glider.

Because of me, did human beings build crazy gliders without benefit of engineering, and kill themselves therewith? I wouldn't be a bit surprised. Am I callous that the thought doesn't bother me, or merely normal? Someone else would have written for Gernsback if I hadn't, and probably would have written just as badly. Truthfully, the only guilt I feel concerning *How to Build and Fly Gliders* is for the atrocious English in which it is written.

A REAL SAILPLANE

During my first two years at Caltech, I thought that I had plenty of spare time. I continued to glide with maniacal enthusiasm. The first year, two other Caltech fellows and I (with the part-time help of an erratic Russian named Nick Scaredoff) built a two-place tandem open-framed training glider. It flew just fairly well. I report only two anecdotes concerning it. In it, I took my mother up. She was game for anything. Using it, we tried to teach Nick Scaredoff to fly.

I don't believe that Nick really wanted to fly, but his pride forbade him to decline. We stretched the shock cord out and catapulted him into the air, above a gentle slope. Nick obeyed instructions until the glider first touched his dearly beloved earth. He then concluded that the flight was over and made hasty motions to get out. The glider was still on its way, and when he released the stick it reared up and turned clean over. Nick was strapped in, so only the glider was hurt and it so slightly that we soon repaired it.

The two-place glider was just practice. I wanted a sailplane. I was a little if not much wiser by now, and what I built was sensible if not truly engineered. It had a tapered wing with a 45-foot span. The center ten feet had a four-foot cord, and the wing tapered to two feet at the tips. The wing was braced with short struts. It lay atop a sleek, narrow fuselage into which I could barely crawl.

It had been a wonderful thing to hang out in the air, with nothing visible but the world below, perched on the slender skid of the old glider. But it was thrilling, too, to fly faster and farther, whistling through the air in my bright silver sailplane. A mere touch of the controls and it tipped and dipped, so ignorant was I of proper aerodynamic design. In this plane I would really fly.

FRED COMER

Fred Comer was a help to everyone. Known to himself as The Long Hork, by which he meant a species of bird, he was always willing to pull on the shock cord or to help load a glider onto the trailer to be pulled back up the hill. Fred presented me with some goggles and an aluminum box to hold them. The box, according to the trademark, originally contained an athletic supporter. The goggles were a useful gift, for while flying my sailplane I could scarcely see for the tears in my eyes.

Fred could fly, too. He worked for a man with an airplane, caring for the ship and occasionally getting a turn at the controls. I liked Fred, and one day I let him fly my lovely sailplane.

In those days we flew off a slope at the north of the Palos Verdes Hills, a slope overlooking Redondo. Today it is covered with houses. For short flights there we used the round crown, a long gentle slope, and a good flat stretch short of the highway to land on.

Beyond the highway there was a fine dune about 50 feet high with a cliff just beyond; in the rising currents, one could soar.

Fred set out in fine style, clearing the dune at a great height. He executed part of a turn, but heading downwind his senses deceived him. He judged that he had flying speed, and he didn't. He stalled, executed a half turn of a flat spin, and went into the ground on wing and nose.

The front of the fuselage was crushed and Fred was thrown clear. The spar of one wing was cracked. When I reached my beloved sailplane in full career I was not quite rational. I was terribly annoyed that good, kind, useful Fred was completely unhurt.

I REALLY SOAR

The sailplane's injuries were serious but not fatal. I patched the spar with plywood. I built a new, narrower, and shorter fuselage which made the controls even more sensitive. One clear, fine day, when the wind blew strongly from the ocean, I flew out over the dune and turned left. The wind lifted me, and when I came to the end of the dune I turned out into the wind, clear around, and back over the dune again. My broad, sloppy turn, with too much diving to avoid stalling, cost me altitude, but this I quickly regained. Soon I had made another turn and then another. I was soaring, and learning more than I had in months. The wind was whistling past me. I was diving. I didn't have to go so fast. So I pulled back, and flew higher still. This was all that I had been waiting for, but I am not sure that I enjoyed it with full consciousness. I was too intent on what I was doing. There was the dune. There was the blue sea.

There was the hill and the crowd. I saw flashes of each, and all the time there was I, hundreds of feet in the air, turning, rising, turning, rising, learning to fly my sailplane in an endless series of figure eights.

Suddenly I noticed that there was another glider below me, a long-winged machine with a boom tail, which belonged to Vick Evans. It was doing its own endless series of figure eights between me and the dune.

This worried me, because I could see Vick only part of the time, and I mistrusted my skill. So, after a few more turns, I flew behind the dune and landed, just 29 minutes after I had taken off. As I got out of the cockpit, dizzy from my experience, I looked up at Evans' ship. He was just diving down toward the crowd to amuse them. As he pulled up suddenly, the wings folded above the ship, and it struck the ground with a rending crash. "There goes Vick!" shouted a friend as he rushed past me.

DEATH OF A NEIGHBOR

I went slowly toward the wreckage. I didn't want to face the scene or to help, and yet a sense of obligation drove me on. When I arrived, they had got Vick out and laid him on the ground. He was bloody and quiescent. Suddenly, his hands and knees jerked forward in a scrabbling motion. Then he collapsed and was quiet and limp. His friends put him into a car and took him off, but I was sure that he was dead.

Vick was not the only one among my friends or acquaintances who was killed in a glider. Sometime before, a man in San Francisco had had himself towed aloft behind an airplane in his training glider. He had allowed the tow rope to go slack, and the airplane had jerked the skid and the man away from the wings. In a newsreel I saw him falling through the air, all, all alone.

This had been his foolishness, for we all knew that Dale Drake had flown more than a hundred miles behind a plane. He was a good pilot, and he had a ship designed to glide well.

Vick's death was closer to home. And then, there was the case of the nice fellow whose name I no longer remember. He was not killed. He had built a beautiful sailplane, but it had some sort of aerodynamic instability, so that once in a shallow dive it couldn't be pulled out. His leg was broken, and I sat beside him and talked to him until they brought a doctor.

The other deaths are more remote. I had another sailplane, which I had bought partially completed. When I took it out to try for the first time, I saw a pile of wreckage at the bottom of the hill. "What's that?" I asked. "The Riverside High School boys built it," someone replied. Jimmy Caruso had tested it for them. He died on the way to the hospital.

I flew the sailplane that day. I was not reassured when at the end of a later flight the flimsy wings broke off on landing.

I was a pallbearer at Jimmy's funeral, along with his partner, Ray Chesley, Apollo Smith, and other enthusiasts. We listened uncomprehendingly to the discourse of the priest, who spoke movingly of the efficacy of prayer for the dead. Jimmy hadn't been a very good Catholic. We listened in embarrassed silence to the piercing wails of Jimmy's mother.

The other boys and I shocked the undertaker by our irreverence as we drove to the cemetery. Inside, we were scared.

Apollo and his father had built a wonderfully big and wonderfully light sailplane, and they let an acquaintance of mine, a man named White, take it up. High in the air, he had some sort of fainting fit to which he was subject. He was killed in the crash. He left a wife and a small son.

With the passing of time, Frank Slaughter completed his sailplane. The gnawed-away spars and the improperly braced fuselage were covered with cloth which he painted handsomely in many colors. When Frank offered to let me fly it, I declined without visibly shuddering. Frank flew it. One day, the tail fell off, and the wing landed on the back of his head, pushing his glasses clear into his face. The mortician made the powdered face look quite human, but it didn't look at all like Frank.

Once a very young and flighty enthusiast said to me, "In our clubhouse we've got a board with clippings about Jimmy, and Vick, and Frank, and the rest of them. We've got a place for everyone. We're saving a place for you."

I sold my gliders and built a 14-foot boat out of quarter-inch plywood. In it I went sailing on the ocean.

I flew a few times more, when someone invited me. To this day, when I look down a fine slope, over fields and houses, with the wind in my face, I long for wings. I long to soar out over it all. I won't seek this. But I do believe that if the chance came unsought, I would fly.

NOTE

[1] National Advisory Committee for Aeronautics, the predecessor of NASA.

II
Way Out

This section gives an inside account of satellite communication as it seemed before the launching of any satellites, while experimental communication satellites were being launched, and as it seems now that satellite communication is a commercial reality.

Don't Write: Telegraph*

SOMETIMES it seems to me that science fiction writers are eternally bent on straining at gnats while they swallow camels. Their atomic-powered rocket ships easily attain a velocity near to that of light despite the fact that elementary calculations show how ridiculous this is. Thousands of feet—board feet?—of lumber are shipped to Mars by an author who seems overwhelmed at the cost of sending one letter. A janitor on the Moon can afford to exchange only an occasional telautograph (!) with his son, and so on and on and on.

There is something strangely perverse, too, in this archaic idea of sending letters from planet to planet. Why a letter? Why carry the tradition of the courier as developed through the United States Post Office clear across space to the planets? Why waste pounds of fuel to transport costly ounces of freight, when a fraction of the energy would whisk the impalpable essence of the message planetward at the speed of light, safe from hostile leagues, or even B.E.M.'s?

And what is this heresy about Mars ships and Mars expeditions being out of touch with Earth? Why should it be expensive to communicate even with our nearest neighbor, the Moon, which is in sight, separated from us only by the equivalent of five miles of sea-level atmosphere and the rest clear empty space? Why, the Moon is even within radar range! We know from our own experience that one can wire the Pacific Coast cheaply, and this despite hazards of storm and atmosphere which would put it clean out of sight even if it weren't for the curvature of the earth.

The truth is that you could order equipment for an Earth-Moon link from any of several manufacturers. The plain truth is that any communication engineer would give his eye teeth to have the cheap

* Reprinted by permission of John R. Pierce from *Astounding Science Fiction* (now *Analog Science Fiction—Science Fact*) ; copyright © 1952, by Street & Smith Publications, Inc., March, 1952.

and easy Earth-Moon path to span rather than the tough coast-to-coast path. The fact is that, granted a base on the Moon, transatlantic television would be a snap rather than an almost insuperably difficult problem. And some sort of radio link to Mars wouldn't be hard, either.

Perhaps readers of *Astounding Science Fiction*[1] would like to know the facts about interplanetary communication: why it is easy by very standard methods at a time when even the Moon rocket is largely wishful thinking.

For proper orientation it is best to start with the problems of earthly communication over long distances, in order to appreciate the advantages of line-of-sight paths through a vacuum.

How do we telegraph or talk across the continent? By wire or by radio. Now we can't lay wires to the planets, but wires are worth a thought for the sake of contrast. For instance, the most advanced and economical sort of wire communication makes use of the coaxial cable, in which about 600^2 telephone messages are sent through a hollow copper tube with a central inner wire. To span the continent, thousands of miles of this cable must be plowed into the ground. And, every eight miles a vacuum-tube[3] repeater must be used to amplify the signal. That means some 500 repeaters in all over the longest, somewhat indirect route. Each repeater consumes power, and each adds noise and distortion. Imagine the difficulty and cost of such a system! And yet, granted heavy traffic, coaxial cable is the cheapest form of transcontinental wire communication.

It is clear that point-to-point radio must be cheaper, for it requires only a transmitter and a receiver to span thousands of miles. Indeed, it would be, but:

Short wave is unreliable. Short-wave radio can span long distances only because the radio waves are reflected from the ionized Heaviside layer. The Heaviside layer is erratic. It changes slowly all the time and violently during magnetic storms. Partly, changes in it can be compensated for by changing frequency in the range from 3 to 20 megacycles per second. Thus, in short-wave transmission one must hunt around, frequency-wise, for the best transmission. But even then one can't always get through. This is especially so in the arctic regions. Telegraph and telephone are good to South America and the South Pacific. Telegraph is good to northern Europe but telephone is pretty unreliable and the quality is bad. Both telegraph and telephone to the arctic are unreliable.

Even at the best, short-wave signals are poor enough, and they are no good at all for television.

Worst of all, the short waves are crowded. No one would think of using them when anything more reliable is available, but nothing else is available for many purposes, such as communication with ships, communication with remote locations, and telephony over oceans. And these uses mean that the short-wave band of frequencies is severely overcrowded.

Besides wire and short waves, we have a newer art of earthly communication: microwave radio. Microwaves are unaffected by the Heaviside layer—the "ionosphere" to moderns—though on calm summer nights they are sometimes seriously disturbed by stratified atmospheric layers lying over the earth, and they can be attenuated by rain. But, largely, microwaves travel in straight lines, right through rain, fog, and storm. In going across the country, the American Telephone and Telegraph Company's transcontinental microwave radio relay system uses 107 hilltop relay stations, each in sight of its neighbors about 30 miles away.

Microwave radio is probably the cheapest way to get television from coast to coast, but what disadvantages it has here on earth!

Because line-of-sight paths are needed, one can go only about 30 miles on the average, and there one must supply an expensive repeater station, complete with ac power and with standby generating equipment as well. And, because one must have repeaters to cross the country, each adding an equal share of noise to the signal, the power transmitted at each must be 107 times that needed to span a single link.

Further, the combination of atmospheric conditions and reflections from Earth, or atmospheric conditions alone, for that matter, cause fading of the signal, and around a hundred times the power which would otherwise be needed must be transmitted to allow for this.

Despite the curvature of the earth, which necessitates many repeater stations, each adding its share of noise, and despite the fading caused by the presence of our atmosphere, coast-to-coast television and telephone communication are being carried out by microwave radio.

Now, as a rough guide, it is interesting to know how much power is required at the transmitter of a microwave radio repeater in a system of the type described. Remember, the power is increased by a factor of around one hundred to allow for noise in other links, and by another factor of around one hundred to allow for fading. Yet, the power required is—half a watt! It is this ridiculously small power requirement that gives hope for interplanetary communication by microwaves.

Communication beyond Earth is difficult almost solely because of distance. For microwaves our atmosphere—the equivalent of five miles at sea-level pressure—makes little difference. The usual sources of fading interfere with horizontally directed rather than vertically directed signals. The amount of rain seen looking upward is probably never enough to affect seriously a signal of wave length longer than two centimeters, and atmospheric absorption is certainly negligible at wave lengths longer than this. Hence, for wave lengths in the usual microwave range we have only distance to consider.

Distance comes in three distinct steps: the distance to our Moon, the distance to the planets, and the distance to the stars. A microwave signal spreads out through space as a conical beam with the point at the transmitter. Thus, as the signal travels, its power is spread out over an area which increases as the square of the distance traveled. Hence, the power required varies as the square of the path length between transmitter and receiver. We can easily evaluate the relative powers required for various paths, taking the Earth-Moon path as a standard of comparison. Table I gives the answers:

TABLE I			
Communication to:	Distance, millions of miles	Relative power	Time of travel
Moon	.239	1	1.3 sec
Mars, opposition	35	22,400	3.1 min
Mars, conjunction	144	363,000	12.8 min
Alpha Centauri	2.5×10^7	1.1×10^{16}	4.3 years

In Table I, 1.1×10^{16} means that the number 1.1 should be multiplied by the number 1 followed by 16 zeroes, or 10,000,000,000,000,000.

The data in Table I must be supplemented by other data: how much power do we need at the microwave receiver, and what fraction of the transmitter power is received? The power needed at the microwave receiver is dependent on two things: the noise received along with the signal, and noise generated in the receiver itself.

A bright light near the Sun would have to be very bright indeed to be seen. Similarly, a microwave transmitter near a very hot star would suffer interference from the microwave energy radiated by the star. As it happens, however, the chief source of noise in microwave transmission is the noise generated in the receiver. If a highly directive receiving antenna was pointed directly at our Sun, the noise received would just about equal the noise generated in a good microwave receiver, and noise received from other parts of the heavens is negligible in comparison. Hence, we can design our microwave link on the assumption that the noise to be overcome is that generated in the receiver alone. Table II isn't too far astray.

TABLE II			
Type of communication	Bandwidth in cycles per second	Signal-to-noise power ratio, times	Power required at receiver, watts
teletype	170	100	6.8×10^{-16}
telephone	4,000	10,000	1.6×10^{-12}
television	4,000,000	10,000	1.6×10^{-9}

The other figure required is the path loss, or the ratio of power received to power transmitted.

Microwave antennas are reflectors or horns which receive power over a rather large area and guide it to the receiver. Clearly, the larger the receiving antenna, the greater the fraction of the transmitted signal which is received, regardless of the wave length used. Thus, the larger the receiving antenna, the less the path loss, and the less the transmitted power which is needed.

Increasing the size of the transmitting antenna, horn or reflector as it may be, narrows the width of the conical beam of microwaves which the transmitter sends out and hence increases the strength of the signal at the receiving antenna. Thus, the larger the transmitting antenna, the less the path loss.

Clearly, we want to use big antennas, but how big can we make them? The biggest microwave antenna made so far is the radio telescope at the Naval Research Laboratory, a parabolic reflector 50 feet in diameter, with an area of 1,960 square feet.

Assuming transmitting and receiving antennas of 1,000 square feet effective area, a wave length of 0.1 feet, and a distance of 0.239 million miles or 1,260 million feet, we obtain for the ratio of transmitted power to received power

$$\frac{P_T}{P_R} = 1.6 \times 10^{10}$$

We have still not determined the power required to send a message anywhere. To get the transmitter power required for a Moon link, we need only multiply the power figures of Table II by 1.6×10^{10}. This gives the powers listed in Table III.

TABLE III
Power for Earth-Moon link, 3 cm wave
length, 50 foot antennas

Type of communication	Power in watts
teletype	10.9×10^{-6}
telephone	25.6×10^{-3}
television	25.6

From Earth to the Moon with ten millionths of a watt? Isn't there something a little unreasonable about this? As a matter of fact, there is. The figures given are based on what is called single-sideband transmission. At microwaves, such transmission is very difficult and perhaps impossible at present for bandwidths as narrow as the 170 cycles per second assumed for teletype. The point is, however, that no one would think of trying to use single-sideband transmission unless he simply had to. In any case, no one would think of setting up a 50-foot antenna and feeding it with only ten microwatts. He would probably choose to use at least ten watts, which should be a small amount of power even on the Moon.

The figures for telephony and television are not optimistic although they are based on single-sideband transmission. For instance, a high-deviation frequency-modulation system would require even less power than the narrow-band single-sideband system which I have assumed. Thus, ten watts would be enough for 400 independent telephone channels. Actually, it would do for about 4,000 telephone channels, taking into account the fact that talkers talk lower than peak loudness or are silent most of the time. As each telephone channel can, according to present-day earthly practice, carry 18 teletype channels, ten watts could provide 7,200 teletype channels between Earth and the Moon—teletype talks loud all the time.

What about communication to spaceships? Assume that we have a 50-foot antenna on Earth and use only one watt of power on the spaceship. This means we would have 40 times the power we need for telephony with a 50-foot antenna on the ship. We can cut the antenna area down to $1/40$ of that of a 50-foot antenna, giving an antenna diameter of eight feet. Or, with ten watts of power we could do with an antenna 2.5 feet in diameter!

What would a reasonable Moon link cost to operate? This is a very iffy question which we can tackle only by the method of unwarranted assumptions. We will consider a very unfavorable case, that in the early days of Earth-Moon communication, when the traffic is light. We will consider only the cost of transmission between a central point on Earth and a central point on the Moon.

Even in this simple case it will be hard enough to estimate costs on Earth, but what about costs on the Moon? For no particular reason I shall assume that everything on the Moon costs nine times what it does on Earth. This will make the total cost ten times the cost attributable to the Earth station and its operation alone.

What, then, about the Earthside cost? Suppose we design our system for one telephone channel or for 18 teletype channels. If we use ten watts' transmitter power at each end, the antennas at each end have to be only ten feet in diameter. I think that there are companies which would build an appropriate station for $100,000 or less, but suppose that we assume it to cost half a million dollars. We will assume depreciation over a ten-year period, and this and interest will amount to about $75,000 a year. Another $25,000 should certainly take care of maintenance and operation. Thus, the terminal itself might cost $100,000 a year.

How many words can we send for that money? We will be in sight of the Moon 12 hours a day, or 4,400 hours a year. Although teletype is usually operated at 60 words a minute, a single teletype channel can, when tuned up properly, carry 100 words a minute or 6,000 words an hour, and hence about 26 million words a year. With 18 channels available, we can send about 470 million words a year, and the cost for the Earthside station is thus 0.021 cents per word. Allowing for a total cost of ten times this, the total cost of transmission comes out to be less than a quarter of a cent per word. The cost of *transmission* of a 400-word letter would be less than a dollar.

What about Mars? From Tables I and II we can calculate the powers required, and these are given in Table IV:

TABLE IV		
Power for Earth-Mars link, 3 cm wave length, 50 foot antennas		
Type of communication	Power in watts, opposition	Power in watts, conjunction
teletype	.24	4.0
telephone	570	9,300
television	570,000	9,300,000

The power required for a single telephone channel at opposition is about that which has been produced at three centimeters' wave length; the other powers are larger. Use of preferred methods of transmission such as high-deviation frequency modulation and other expedients, and the use of larger antennas, would somewhat reduce the power required. I think that we could probably make a telephone link to Mars at conjunction now, but television will have to wait for further advances, of which there should be many by the time we get to Mars.

Telephone users will have to wait, in a different sense. Even at opposition, you wouldn't hear the last of the other party's words till 3.1 minutes after he stopped speaking, and it would thus be 6.2 minutes after his last word before he would hear the first word of your reply. This makes telephony as we know it impractical. But one-way voice communication, such as radio broadcast, is practical. So is teletype. If we allow a little time for development, communication with Mars shouldn't cost much more than communication with the Moon would now. You see, what is required is not more links nor more wire, but only a little more power, a little shorter wave length, and antennas which are a little larger. And I think that with reasonable powers one will be able to communicate with a spaceship all the way from Earth to Mars. At least, that certainly seems nearer than does getting to the planet.

What about the stars, which are so very much farther away? If we multiply the 10.9 microwatts of Table III, for a single teletype channel to the Moon, by the factor 1.1×10^{16} from Table I, we reach the gloomy conclusion that it would take 10^{11} or 100,000 million watts to send a teletype message to Alpha Centauri. This is a ridiculous amount of power, even for someone capable of making the journey.

Maybe, however, we are expecting too much. Or, are we being unduly pessimistic? There is a long time for further research before men reach the stars. Let us sweep mere technical difficulties aside. I think that doing this will actually give us the truest picture, for our understanding of what is theoretically attainable in a communication system goes considerably beyond our guesses as to what we can now do in a practical way, let alone what we will be able to do in the near future. What is theoretically attainable is all written out in a book, *The Mathematical Theory of Communication*, by Claude E. Shannon of the Bell Telephone Laboratories and Warren Weaver of the Rockefeller Foundation. In fact, it is contained in a simple formula:

$$R = B \log_2 \frac{(P_S - P_N)}{(P_N)}$$

Here R is the rate at which information can be transmitted, measured in bits per second, B is the bandwidth of the system measured in cycles per second, P_S is the signal power and P_N is the noise power.

What shall we take for noise power? I see no reason that a microwave receiver need generate any appreciable noise at all, and, granted a few thousand years of research and development, why not assume that the noise received is just that radiated from the contents of space: stars, dust and all? I seem to remember that the temperature assigned to space is about four degrees Kelvin, or only 4/293 of the reference noise temperature referred to earlier. Let us assume a bandwidth of ten cycles per second.

We will also assume 100-foot diameter antennas and a wave length of one centimeter. With these assumptions, we find that the ratio of transmitter power to receiver power must be 1.2×10^{24}. Thus, the transmitter power must be this number times the number of watts required at the receiver, which is 5.5×10^{-22} watts. Or, we need a transmitter power of only 650 watts!

To me, this seemed nothing short of astonishing. Of course, I might have underestimated the temperature of space a little, but that couldn't make much difference. Had I neglected anything? What about quantum effects?

Energy comes in little discrete packages, and the energy in each package, measured in joules, is 6.62×10^{-34} times the frequency of the radiation involved. The frequency of a radio wave of one centimeter wave length is 3×10^{10} cycles per second. Hence, the energy per quantum is 2×10^{-23} joules.

Now, we assumed that our receiver receives 5.5×10^{-22} watts of power from the transmitter, and that it receives ten bits of information a second. This means that there are only $5.5 \times^{-23}$ joules per bit, and this in turn means that there are only between two and three quanta allotted to carry one bit of information.

Certainly, quantum effects put our system right on the borderline, and probably 650 watts won't be enough to signal to Alpha Centauri at a rate of ten bits a second with the system described. Maybe we'll need a whole kilowatt to go those 4.3 light-years!

So far, we know that with an essentially ideal communication system using 100-foot antennas and a wave length of one centimeter, around a kilowatt should enable us to send ten bits of information a second to Alpha Centauri. With a very crude form of encoding, this would send two letters a second, 0.4 words a second, or 24 words a minute. With a more efficient form of encoding, it might be possible to triple the rate and send about 72 words a minute. This should serve to while away the tedium of an interstellar expedition.

Could we do this right now? No! We don't have the noise-free microwave receiver described.[4] We don't know just what sort of modulation and encoding to use. We don't know how to receive a signal at noise level, with a bandwidth of only ten cycles per second, and that despite a large Doppler shift of frequency due to relative motion of transmitter and receiver. But we don't know how to reach Alpha Centauri now either, and that with a lot more emphasis. The difficulty will be in getting to the stars, not in telegraphing home about it!

NOTES

[1] See note on p. 29.

[2] 3,600 in 1966.

[3] Transistor in 1966.

[4] This is the maser, invented by C. H. Townes in 1955.

Orbital Radio Relays*

ABSTRACT

WHILE orbital radio relays probably could not compete with microwave radio relay for communication over land, they might be useful in transoceanic communication. Three sorts of repeaters appear to be consistent with microwave art: (a) 100-foot reflecting spheres at an altitude of around 2,200 miles; (b) a 100-foot oriented plane mirror in a 24-hour orbit, at an altitude of 22,000 miles; (c) an active repeater in a 24-hour orbit. Cases (a) and (b) require at 10-cm wavelength 250-foot diameter antennas and 100-kW and 50-kW power, respectively; in case (c), using 250-foot antennas on the ground and 10-foot antennas on the repeater, only 100 watts on the ground and 0.03 watt on the repeater would be required; in this case one should probably use smaller antennas on the ground. In cases (b) and (c), the problem of maintaining the correct orientation and position of the repeater is critical; perturbations by the Moon and Sun might cause the satellite to rock or wander prohibitively.

INTRODUCTION

Following the announcement last year that the American Telephone and Telegraph Company and the British Post Office have jointly undertaken the construction of a 36-channel two-way submarine telephone cable across the Atlantic at a cost of 35 million dollars, it is natural, at least for a person who is a complete amateur in such matters, to speculate about further developments in transoceanic communication, even into the far future.

Would a channel 30 times as wide, which would accommodate 1,080 phone conversations or one television signal, be worth 30×35

*Reprinted with permission from *Jet Propulsion*, April, 1955; copyright © 1955, by the American Rocket Society, Inc.

million dollars; that is, a billion dollars? Will someone spend this much trying to make a broadband channel to Europe? The idea is of course absurd. At the present, there is no commercial demand which would justify such a channel. By the time there is, surely some technical solution to the problem will be sought which does not involve multiplying the cost of the present cable in proportion to the bandwidth.

It is conceivable that such a solution could come about through further development in the field of cables, but a very difficult step must be taken to multiply the channel capacity by 30 or more. In the meantime, other means for obtaining a broadband channel to Europe have been considered, including routes largely across land rather than across water.

A route from Labrador or Baffin Island to Greenland, around the coast of Greenland, thence to Iceland and, via the Faroe Islands, to Scotland traverses much nasty country by land and still leaves gaps of several hundred miles by sea. These gaps might conceivably be spanned by radio, using very high power. Perhaps it may be possible to make undersea television cables which would span gaps of a few hundred miles before such cables can be made to span thousands of miles. Even granting the success of a difficult radio link or a broadband cable, both terrain and climate make this indirect route difficult and unappealing.

A route from Alaska across the Bering Strait to Siberia, and thence overland to Europe is conceivable, but it is difficult and indirect and it has other disadvantages which need not be mentioned.

Radio relay along a continual chain of planes crossing the Atlantic has been proposed. While this is certainly technically feasible, in good weather at least, it seems strange either as a long-range or a short-range solution.

Another "solution" has been proposed to the problem of transoceanic communication, that is, relaying by means of a satellite revolving about the earth above the atmosphere. Many engineers do not doubt that it will eventually be possible to put a satellite up and into place, and to supply it with small amounts of power for long periods and to exercise some sort of radio control over it. However, there is no unclassified information in regard to how long it will be before a satellite could be put up or what it might cost to do so, and there may not even be classified information on the subject. Thus, although some aspects of transoceanic communication via a satellite are being considered in this paper, nothing can be said at this point about the over-all feasibility of such communication, which must depend on the feasibility of the satellite itself.

Fortunately, there is a good deal else to be said about the matter. For instance, only *transoceanic* communication has been mentioned, and for a reason. There are at present transcontinental television circuits. The announced cost of the American Telephone and Telegraph Company's transcontinental TD2 microwave system was 40 million dollars. This is only 5 million dollars more than the 35 million for the 36-channel transatlantic cable, and yet the TD2 system provides a number of television channels in both directions, as well as many telephone channels. Perhaps even more important in an overland system, it provides facilities for dropping and adding channels along the route. Without such flexibility, an overland system would be almost useless.

Some types of satellite relay systems would provide communication only between selected points. These would lack the flexibility required for overland service. Further, there is little reason to believe that a satellite relay could compete with present microwave radio relay or coaxial cable in cost. Present facilities are very satisfactory, so that there is little incentive to replace them with some difficult alternative system, even if it could do the same job. Thus, satellite radio relay seems attractive only for spanning oceans.

Two different sorts of satellite radio repeaters suggest themselves. One consists of enough spheres in relatively near orbits so that one of them is always in sight at the transmitting and receiving locations. This sphere isotropically scatters the transmitted signal, so one has merely to point the transmitter and receiver antennas at it to complete the path. Another system uses a plane mirror or an active repeater with a 24-hour orbital period, located directly above the equator at a radius of around 26,000 miles or an altitude of about 22,000 miles. Such a satellite would be visible to within nine degrees of the poles; that is, in all inhabited latitudes. If it were not for the perturbations of the orbit by the Moon and the Sun, it could stay fixed relative to the surface of the Earth, and large fixed antennas could be used on Earth. However, it appears that perturbation of the orbit would be large enough to necessitate steerable antennas on Earth and orientation of the satellite antennas or the reflector by remote control.

Even disregarding problems concerned with the making and placing of the satellites, would such satellite relay systems or any satellite relay system be feasible in other respects? To decide this, two sorts of problems must be considered: problems of microwave communication, and problems lying in the field of celestial mechanics, concerned with the orbit and orientation of a satellite.

PROBLEMS OF MICROWAVE COMMUNICATION

Allowable path loss is a dominating consideration in a satellite radio relay system, and the allowable path loss depends on the system of modulation used. Systems of modulation such as binary pulse code modulation, which require small power but large bandwidth, seem particularly suitable. Figures concerning the received power required are shown in Table I.

TABLE I	
Modulation	8 digit binary PCM
Video bandwidth	5 Mc
RF bandwidth	40 Mc
RF signal-to-noise	20 dB
RF noise figure	6 dB
RF received signal	—102 dBw

Using the power given in Table I, the allowable path loss versus transmitter power can now be tabulated, as in Table II.

TABLE II	
Transmitter power, watts	Allowable path loss, dB
0.01	82
0.1	92
1	102
10	112
100	122
1,000	132
10,000	142
100,000	152
1,000,000	162
10,000,000	172

REPEATERS

PASSIVE REPEATERS

Passive repeaters are very attractive in many ways. They would require no maintenance and they would be almost immune to meteor damage. It will be shown that some kinds might require remote control devices for orientation, but these could be simple.

Isotropic Reflectors

One type of passive repeater which will be considered is a sphere, which acts as an isotropic reflector and scatters the intercepted power equally in all directions. Such a repeater is of use between any two locations in sight of it.

Circular transmitting and receiving antennas with diameters of 250 feet, a sphere with a diameter of 1,000 feet and a wavelength of 10 cm are considered. For a range of 22,000 miles the path loss will be 171 dB. Referring to Table II, it is seen that this would require a power of around 10 megawatts. Even allowing for the fact that a transmitter for binary PCM is on only half the time on the average, this seems a ridiculously high figure.

Going to a wavelength of 3 cm would cut the power requirement down by a factor of 10, but the power required still seems much too high.

The use of a number of spheres at some lower altitude might also be examined. There will certainly be a need to transmit over a total path length of thousands of miles. If, for example, a distance to the sphere of 2,200 miles is taken, instead of 22,000 miles, then from Equation [2.3] it is seen that this would decrease the path loss by only 40 dB, making the power requirement 1 kilowatt. However, a multiplicity of spheres is now needed, and perhaps a diameter of 1,000 feet is unreasonable (even for one sphere). Cutting the diameter of the spheres to 100 feet would raise the power by 20 dB, calling for 100 kW at 10-cm wavelength.

A Plane Mirror

Suppose that a slightly concave mirror is used as a passive repeater. This could act as a perfectly focused transmitting and receiving antenna. If it is assumed, as it has been, that the transmitting antenna and the receiving antenna are equidistant from the mirror and 22,000 miles away from it, then the radius of curvature of the mirror should be 22,000 miles.

Again considering a 10-cm wavelength, 250-foot circular antenna and a 100-foot circular mirror, a path loss of $(P_R/P_T)_2 = 139$ dB is computed. According to Table II, this would allow operation with a power of 50,000 watts.

In using a plane mirror there is a serious problem of satellite position and orientation. With a 100-foot mirror and a 10-cm wavelength, the beam is only 0.19 degrees wide, which means that the mirror must be oriented to less than half of this angle, and the beam is only 72 miles wide at the surface of the Earth.

A Corner Reflector

Suppose there is a corner reflector in a 22,000-mile equatorial orbit. Wherever this could be seen, it could be used to broadcast in the vicinity of the transmitter, for it will send what energy it receives back toward the transmitter. For zero wavelength, radiation would fall over an area as great as that of the corner reflector. To get a reasonable coverage, only a rather small corner reflector can be used—say, 10-foot diameter at a wavelength of 10 cm—and only a small receiving antenna, say, 4-foot diameter. Assuming transmitting antenna 250 feet in diameter, the path loss comes to about 211 dB, which is much too high.

ACTIVE REPEATERS

The big advantage of an active repeater is that the size and directivity can be relatively small. Thus, the orientation need not be as accurate as in the case of a plane reflector. It would seem desirable to make the repeater as small and as low-powered as possible, and hence one should perhaps use as large a receiving antenna on Earth as seems reasonable. Thus, an antenna diameter of 250 feet will be assumed, as in the case of passive repeaters. A repeater antenna 10 feet in diameter will be assumed.

Referring to Table I, it is seen that this would require a transmitter power of only 0.03 watt or 30 milliwatts.

What about the link from Earth to the satellite? Assume that a 250-foot transmitting antenna, a 10-foot receiving antenna, and transmitter power of 100 watts are used. Then the noise figure of the satellite receiver could be over 40 dB, and the gain required would be only 52 dB.

With these requirements, a single low-voltage, low-performance traveling-wave tube should be quite adequate. Such a tube could be designed for very low cathode current density, and hence for long life. It could be operated by solar batteries if some sort of storage could be provided. A 30-milliwatt traveling-wave tube, exclusive of power supplies, could weigh 2 pounds or less. Its power consumption, chiefly cathode power, could be 5 watts or less.

SOME MECHANICAL AND ASTRONOMICAL PROBLEMS

While no consideration will be given to the actual problem of getting a satellite into position, some consideration should be given to mechanical and astronomical problems before any comparison is made among the various systems discussed in the preceding section.

WEIGHT

There now follows a very rough examination of what the weight of metallic spheres and mirrors might be.

Aluminum weighs 168.5 lb/ft^3. The area of a 100-foot circle is 7,850 $feet^2$ and that of a 100-foot sphere is 4 times this. If the foil were 1 mil thick, the weight of the 100-foot mirror would be 110 pounds and that of a 100-foot sphere would be 440 pounds. The weight of a 1,000-foot sphere would be 100 times as much, or 44,000 pounds.

The mirror would have to be stretched on a frame which would weigh several hundred pounds.

To keep the sphere spherical, initially one could inflate it gently. Thereafter, loss of pressure because of meteor puncture would be expected. The spherical shape could be maintained either by straining the skin in the initial inflation, or by fastening to the sphere a beta emitter, so that the sphere would become positively charged and maintain its shape by means of electrostatic repulsion.

As opposed to the sphere, the mirror might be made out of mesh (e.g., tungsten mesh), with openings small compared with a wavelength.

ORBIT

A sphere need only be put into the proper orbit. For a 24-hour orbit, intended to keep the sphere fixed in the sky, this would have to be done with considerable accuracy. An error of altitude of 1 foot would cause a drift out of position of 0.65 mile/year. If a drift of 10,000 miles (about 30 degrees in 50 years) is allowed, the altitude would have to be accurate to about 300 feet. It is possible to measure the altitude much more accurately than this by means of radar, if only the astronomers can tell accurately what altitude the satellite should be put at.

There may, then, be envisioned an unmanned rocket maneuvered into position over a period of time by remote control guided by radar. Either the rocket could itself become the desired satellite by sprouting antennas or a reflector, or it could blow up a sphere and release it.

The subsequent orbit of the satellite is a problem for the astronomers. It would be very interesting to know how far about the sky a 24-foot "fixed" satellite would wander under the influence of the Moon and the Sun.

ORIENTATION

A sphere need not be oriented in its orbit, but a satellite bearing a passive reflector or antennas would have to maintain a fixed orientation with respect to the surface of the Earth.

It is not entirely out of the question to maintain such orientation automatically without expenditure of power. Consider a long beam revolving in an orbit. If it is in a radial orientation and is rotated slightly, there will be a restoring force tending to return it to radial orientation. The genesis of this force is easy to see. In the radial orientation the gravitational force on the outer portions is less than that on the inner portions, while the centrifugal force on the outer portions is greater than that on the inner portions. The beam is under tension. If the beam is rotated so as to bring the outer portions in, there is a couple acting against this rotation.

If the beam were forced to be normal to the radial direction, there would be a couple tending to align it in the plane of the equator because the gravitation forces and the centrifugal forces do not act toward the same center. For a given angular displacement, this couple is less than that tending to align the beam radially.

A long, pointed isosceles triangle would tend to orient itself in the plane of the equator with the pointed end pointing radially in or out. More generally, of the principal axes of inertia, that about which the moment of inertia is greatest would tend to align itself parallel to the Earth's axis, and that about which the moment of inertia is least would tend to align itself radially.

If the body were released in any different orientation it would oscillate forever about this preferred orientation unless damping were provided. The damping could be in the form of viscous liquid in a partly filled tube or container, or, preferably, unbalanced mechanical devices resonant at the frequencies of the natural oscillations of the body about its principal axes.

The natural period of oscillation can be calculated in a straightforward manner. For example, a simple body consisting of two equal masses connected with a rigid rod would tend to orient itself with the rod directed toward the center of the Earth, and if slightly displaced in the equatorial plane it will oscillate with a period τ:

$$\tau = 2\pi \left(\frac{r_0}{3g_0}\right)^{\frac{1}{2}} \cdot \left(\frac{r}{r_0}\right)^{\frac{3}{2}} = 0.84 \left(\frac{r}{r_0}\right)^{\frac{3}{2}} \text{ hr}$$

where g_0 is the standard gravitational acceleration, r_0 is the radius of the Earth, and r is the radial distance to the body. At 22,000 miles, the period would be 11 hours.

By fastening a mirror to a properly proportioned structure provided with damping, the mirror should automatically assume a fixed orientation with respect to the surface of the Earth.

Perturbations by the Moon both in the orbit and in the orientation of the repeaters would certainly rule out an automatic orientation. However, there might still be considered a remotely operated radio-controlled device which could correct orientation by shifting weights. Such a device could use transistors, very small motors, and perhaps solar batteries for power. The operation would be slow and intermittent. The control could be through very high-power pulsed signals, so as to call for a small low-directivity antenna on the satellite. The total power required might be less than for a relay receiver and transmitter.

SUMMARY AND DISCUSSION

A number of problems in connection with satellite repeaters have been discussed in the previous sections. Endless variations and refinements could be made in assumptions. Perhaps frequency of operation and the antenna size should be considerably different from what has been assumed. However, the feasibility and cost of placing various sorts of satellites, which has not been, nor could be, discussed, would certainly strongly influence the nature and the size of satellite one might use.

Thus, the best that can be done is an attempt to state some sort of conclusions concerning the sorts of systems which have been described.

To aid in this discussion, some of the data arrived at earlier have been summarized in Table III. All these are for a 5-Mc video channel provided by an 8-digit binary pulse code modulation system, as described in Table I, and a wavelength of 10 cm. The diameter of the antennas on Earth is assumed to be 250 feet.

The great advantages of the passive repeaters over active repeaters are potential channel capacity and flexibility. Once in place, passive repeaters could be used to provide an almost unlimited number of two-way channels between various points at various wavelengths. They would also allow for modifications and improvements in the ground equipment without changes in the repeater.

TABLE III				
Path length, miles	Repeater description	Power on earth	Repeater output	Orientation must be better than
22,000	1,000 ft sphere	10 megawatts	0	No orientation
2,200	100-ft sphere	100 kW	0	No orientation
22,000	100-ft mirror	50 kW	0	± 18 miles ± 0.047 degree
22,000	10-ft antennas	100 watts	30 mw	± 360 miles ± 0.95 degree

Spheres, which reflect isotropically, are the most flexible of passive repeaters, because they allow transmission between any two points in sight of them. Moreover, with spheres there is no problem of the angular orientation of the repeaters.

For a 24-hour "fixed" repeater and a 1,000-foot sphere, the power required is 10 megawatts, and this seems excessive. However, suppose 10 spheres, each 100 feet in diameter, circled the Earth above the equator at a fairly low altitude. At low latitudes, one or more would always be in sight. The path length would be only about a tenth that for the 24-hour orbit, and the power required would be around 100 kW, which seems quite feasible.

A plane mirror returns much more power than does a sphere of the same diameter. A 100-foot mirror at an altitude of 22,000 miles would call for a transmitter power of about 50 kW, which again is by no means unreasonable.

The great problem in connection with a plane mirror is that of position and orientation. If it were not for the perturbation caused by the Moon and Sun, the position and orientation of the mirror could be preserved automatically by a proper disposition of masses attached to the mirror and by the use of damping.

However, as perturbations of position and orientation will be too large to be tolerated, the orientation of the mirror would have to be adjusted by moving masses through radio control. The power required would be small, perhaps less than that required for an active repeater. The advantage of channel capacity would be preserved.

The plane mirror suffers a considerable limitation compared with the sphere, however. If it really hung fixed in the sky, it would provide communication between any point in sight of its face and another particular corresponding point. However, because perturbation by the Sun and Moon will cause it to wander about in the sky so that the orientation of the mirror must be adjusted to maintain a path between two particular points, a plane mirror can actually be used only to provide channels (and a large number of channels on different frequencies) between two particular points.

The disadvantage of passive repeaters is the great path loss, so that even assuming antennas of a difficult if not prohibitive diameter and accuracy, the power required is large, although probably attainable.

The attractive feature of an active repeater is the small power required and the small antennas needed at the repeater, as well as the small power required at the ground. Indeed, an actual design for an active repeater would probably call for smaller antennas on Earth, perhaps for larger antennas on the satellite, and probably for higher powers on both Earth and satellite. Because the antennas on the satellite would have a comparatively small directivity, and because for a given angular or positional shift the beam from a radiator shifts only half as far as the beam from a reflector, the orientation problem is considerably easier in the case of an active repeater than in the case of a plane reflector. However, there still is an orientation problem, in contrast to the case of a sphere used as a passive repeater.

The chief disadvantage of the active repeater, aside from disadvantages of power supply and life, is that it provides only the number and sort of channels that are built into it. Once it is in place, its channel capacity cannot be substantially increased by anything done on the ground, although some gain might be made by an increase in transmitter power and receiver sensitivity and by a modification of the nature of the signal.

In conclusion, it can be said that, disregarding the feasibility of constructing and placing satellites, it seems that it might be possible to achieve broadband transoceanic communication using satellite repeaters with any one of three general types of repeater: spheres at low altitudes, or a plane reflector, or an active repeater in a 24-hour orbit (at an altitude of around 22,000 miles).

At this point, some information from astronomers about orbits and from rocket men about constructing and placing satellites would be decidedly welcome.

Transoceanic Communication by Means of Satellites*

THE time will certainly come when we shall need a great increase in transoceanic electronic communications. For example, the United States and Western Europe have a wide community of interests and are bound to demand more and more communication facilities across the Atlantic. If we are to be ready to fill these growing needs, we shall have to investigate all promising possibilities.

In doing so, we shall certainly want to keep in mind a rule founded on experience. This rule is that the more telephone circuits we can handle in one bundle, the cheaper they become. Then, too, there is the possibility of requirements for television. In either case, there is a premium on availability of wide bands of frequency.

The submarine cable art is presently distinctly limited in bandwidth. No doubt its capability in this respect will improve as the years go by, but we may well run into economic or technical restrictions not suffered by other techniques.

A chain of UHF scatter links over a northern route might provide channels across the Atlantic Ocean but the quality is dubious, the available bandwidth is limited, and the cost is great. Indeed, we cannot now imagine how one might improve quality of bandwidth while at the same time reducing the costs of such a system. Moreover, such links would not serve for some transoceanic routes.

An undersea millimeter wave system using a round waveguide excited in the TE_{01} mode is a possibility for the remote future, but such a system is far beyond present technology.

* Brief extract from a paper by R. Kompfner, Fellow, IRE, and J. R. Pierce, Fellow, IRE, published in *The Proceedings of the Institute of Radio Engineers*, March, 1959; copyright © 1959, by the Institute of Radio Engineers. Reprinted with permission.

A microwave system using satellite repeaters may have many advantages over the foregoing alternatives. Present rocket technology is at least close to the point of putting in orbit some structure which could act as a reflector or passive repeater. The maser amplifier, which introduces only around a hundredth the noise of earlier amplifiers, cuts down the transmitting power required to a hundredth of that arrived at in an earlier study. This means that a satellite link with attractive properties could be attained within existing microwave art. The cost of a pair of microwave installations at the terminals would probably be less than the cost of a cable of far less bandwidth.

When highly reliable long-life microwave components and power supplies suited to a space environment are available, active repeaters may provide useful communication. When, in addition, accurate enough guidance is available, together with long-life means for adjusting attitude and position in orbit, a "fixed" repeater in a 24-hour orbit could be used.

Obviously, the present state of knowledge is insufficient for the design of a transatlantic satellite communication system of assured performance and cost. Much remains to be learned. For this very reason, and because they appear to be serious contenders for the future, it is important that research on satellite systems be given serious attention.

It should be noted that, in the case of the passive repeater, the bandwidth available is almost unlimited. The passive repeater is a truly linear device, and it can be used simultaneously in many ways, at many frequencies, and with many power levels, without cross talk. Thus, the only cost in adding new channels is that of adding terminals, and these may be of many sorts.

The passive repeater envisioned is a metallized plastic sphere of 100-foot diameter. A considerable amount of work is being done by the National Aeronautics and Space Administration (NASA), which has announced that it will place one or more balloons of this type into orbit sometime in 1959. The major unknown at present is the life of such balloons. Also in question is the ultimate shape.

International Communication and Space*

WHEN we consider relations among the peoples of the world, we are overwhelmingly aware of the divisive forces of conflicting national interests and aspirations and conflicting governmental and economic philosophies. Somehow, the things that most strongly unite the people of a nation seem also most strongly to set nation against nation, so that international agreement on a governmental level is very difficult. Yet there are in the world strong forces that lead to cooperation among people across national boundaries. Science is prominent among these. The need for communication between individuals is another. Except in time of acknowledged war, nations friendly and unfriendly cooperate in maintaining international postal service. And, in electrical communication, both utilitarian art and scientific progress exemplify a flourishing and productive agreement and exchange among the workers of very different nations.

This cooperation takes many forms. Nearly a hundred years ago, what is now the International Telecommunications Union was founded to deal with problems arising from international telegraphy. The ITU is now a part of the United Nations. One of its chief functions has come to be that of reaching international agreements on the allocation of radio frequencies. It is an organization without police powers. Yet, because it deals with matters of common interest among participants whose aims are more scientific and technological than political, it has an admirable record of accomplishment.

Beyond this, international consultative committees of the ITU have arrived at standards of telephone transmission which are recognized and observed internationally. On the scientific side, an independent organization, URSI, the International Scientific Radio

* Originally prepared for broadcast by the Voice of America in a series of *Forum* lectures on "Space Science."

Union, affords national and international exchange of scientific information in the field of radio, and also acts as a scientific consultant to the International Radio Consultative Committee.

Further, the communications agencies of various countries have succeeded in working together harmoniously to provide communication among the peoples of the world. Thus, in my own country, the American Telephone and Telegraph Company has reached international agreements which enable people to telephone to more than 160 different political areas, and AT&T owns transatlantic telephone cables jointly with the British Post Office and with the French and German Post Offices. More than 200 radio telephone circuits connect the United States with overseas points; these circuits use equipment of various designs and manufacture but work together under mutually agreed-upon technical characteristics.

We can see that in its scientific, technological and operational aspects, electrical communication has developed an admirable tradition of international cooperation at all levels. We might hope that this could serve as an attractive example as well as a particular tradition.

Our present means of international electrical communication do not, however, give us as much transoceanic communication as the world needs. While coaxial cables and microwave radio relay systems carry thousands of telephone signals and several television signals across the continent, each transoceanic cable now provides fewer than 100 telephone circuits and no television. Short-wave radio provides a limited number of telephone circuits and no television. We will certainly have submarine cables of improved capacity, but the demand for more transoceanic communication is great and other resources would be welcome.

Today, space science and technology could provide international electrical communication with a new resource potentially useful in linking together more effectively the already highly developed national communication systems of many lands, and ultimately useful in linking together regions of the world which as yet do not even have adequate internal communication.

The realization of satellite communication depends on the exploitation of two arts. One of these is the powerful, reliable, mature art of electrical communication, and of electronics in general. We have seen that this is an international art in both its content and exploitation. If satellite communication depended on this art alone, we could feel confident of a rapid and happy solution of its problems, both technical and international.

But satellite communication requires for its realization another art as well: the new, expensive, and uncertain art of space. We can judge this art in part by the facts that a satellite launching costs several million dollars and that only about half of American launchings have been successful. Satellite communication can come into being only through this art, only through the use of vehicles which have already been developed at great cost by the government primarily for other purposes.

Further, the art of space has only a short and limited history of international cooperation. It is an art with a military background of concealment rather than sharing. It is an art noted more for national braggadocio than for international cooperation. It is an art in which governments feel a strong proprietary interest as a political tool as well as a technological resource.

In the United States, industry is actively engaged in the development of satellite communication systems. Thus, the Bell Telephone Laboratories are working toward a low-altitude multiple-satellite system. The work includes the fabrication and testing of solar cells, traveling-wave tubes, transistors and other components; the construction of an experimental satellite; work on attitude control and other matters, and the construction of a ground terminal near Rumford, Maine. The American Telephone and Telegraph Company has announced that it is willing to bear research costs including launching cost, and its share of the cost of an international satellite communication system. Arrangements have been made with the National Aeronautics and Space Administration for the launching of an experimental satellite at AT&T expense early in 1962. Various other companies, including General Electric, the International Telephone and Telegraph Company, RCA, Hughes, General Telephone and Electronics, and Lockheed have proposed various satellite communication systems.

The U.S. government is also at work in this field, and both civilian and military agencies are active. NASA's Project Relay contemplates the launching of an experimental active communication satellite capable of television transmission in 1962. The goal of the

Army's Advent program is a system using 35,900-kilometers-high stationary satellites, with attitude-control and station-keeping.

Thus, many satellite communication proposals have been made and several government contracts have been let. Yet, the concrete, experimental progress which has been made is limited. There has been much grand planning but little experimental work. Many technical problems must be solved if some of the proposed satellite communication systems are to become practical and economical, and even the simplest systems take us to the very edge of the demonstrated ability of the space art.

Technical problems are not the only problems that must be solved if we are to have useful satellite communication. Satellite communication will be most useful in linking together continental communication systems which are already highly developed. How could an international satellite communication system be operated, and who should pay for it?

Today various continental communications systems are linked together by short-wave radio and by cables. The operating companies and agencies of each country own and operate the terminal facilities in that country. Cables are owned jointly by the agencies or companies which provide service in the countries which the cables connect. Problems concerning frequency allocation are worked out through the International Telecommunications Union.

The cost of an international satellite communication system would be large, but no larger than the cost of a number of underseas cables. Telephone cables now connect the United States with Great Britain, continental Europe, Hawaii, Alaska, Puerto Rico, and Cuba. Cables are being built from the United States to Bermuda, from Puerto Rico to Antigua, and from Florida to Jamaica. A third and broader-band transatlantic cable, to Great Britain, is planned for 1963, and a cable between Hawaii and Japan, for 1964. The British Commonwealth plans a worldwide cable network. The cost of satellite communication could well be borne in the same manner as the cost of such cables.

Thus, satellite communication *could* come into being as an integral part of the international electrical communication which is now effectively serving the world, in a well-established tradition of international scientific, technological, and operational cooperation. This has not been certain, however, for satellite communication must involve the science and technology of space as well as that of communication. There are many people who have regarded the science and technology of space, not as one aspect of the world's long course of scientific and technological progress, but primarily as a unique battleground, in which national prestige or political advantage is to be lost or won.

Such an attitude is dangerous. If we should divorce the science and technology of space from the centuries of science and technology of which it is a part, we would not only misinterpret its nature, we would also abandon successful ways of dealing with real national and international problems and raise a host of new problems which are not truly relevant to the exploitation of the science and technology of space.

Happily, on July 24, 1961, President Kennedy announced a national policy concerning communication satellites which is consistent with their effective and rapid development and use in improving and extending international communication. Mention of the ITU in the statement is a wise acknowledgment of effective existing means of international cooperation. I have every reason to hope that the benefits of satellite communication will be made available to the peoples of the world, perhaps not as soon as we would all like to have them, but at least as quickly as scientific and technical problems allow.

Satellite Science and Technology*

I am neither a historian nor an astronomer, and it would be presumptuous of me to comment at any length either on the life and work of Edmund Halley or on the illustrious men who have delivered the Halley lecture. I cannot help observing, however, the range of interests encompassed in Halley's work, which embraced geomagnetism as well as astronomy; the diligence with which he pursued it; and his bringing, through the publication of Newton's *Principia,* something beyond his own powers to the world of science.

The matters I consider here in connection with satellite science and technology have an even wider range than Halley's work, because science is broader than it was in Halley's day. And, what I discuss is not chiefly my own work, but rather the work of others.

Lest the title of my article be misleading, let me explain that I discuss almost exclusively one sort of satellite among the many that have been launched—that is, satellites intended to explore the possibilities of transoceanic communication. And I further restrict my discussion almost exclusively to two experimental communication satellites: Echo I and TELSTAR I.®

Yet, in dealing with these seemingly specialized satellites, I have something to say about the Earth's atmosphere, both about its temperature and about its density 1,000 miles above the Earth's surface: about the particles trapped in the Earth's magnetic field; about celestial mechanics; about an application of radio astronomy; and about the synchronization of clocks of the Royal Greenwich Observatory at Hurstmonceux, East Sussex, and the United States Naval Observatory at Washington, D.C. I also discuss some findings in the field of

* Adapted from the Halley Lecture delivered at Oxford University on May 15, 1963, and reprinted by permission of John R. Pierce from *Science,* Vol. 141, No. 3577 (July 19, 1963) , 237–44; copyright © 1963 by the American Association for the Advancement of Science.

experimental psychology, and I touch on a remarkable political effect of the Echo and TELSTAR experiments.

Now all this is only a small sample of the multitudinous scientific, technological, and social problems which arose in connection with these communication satellites. Yet I believe that this small sample will show that, if science and technology are only a part of the world of thought, they are a remarkably various and yet highly interrelated part of that world. In dealing with so broad and rambling a subject as the science and technology involved in communication satellites, some sort of organization is necessary.

Since I do not know how else to proceed, I propose to be guided by chronology and to discuss matters in the order in which they became clearly apparent to those connected with the Echo and TELSTAR programs.

Certainly, none of the technical problems would have arisen had there been no overall communication satellite program. For this we must give due credit to Arthur C. Clarke,[1] who in 1945 proposed the relaying and broadcasting of electromagnetic communication signals by means of manned "stationary" satellites at an altitude of 22,300 miles. Yet we see that there is a considerable gap between satellite communication as Clarke proposed it and as it has been realized, for while many people have seen television relayed across the ocean by TELSTAR, the manned space stations which Clarke proposed lie still in the future.

I am sure that echoes of Clarke's words of 1945 had reached my ears (though I had not read the words themselves) when I first thought seriously about satellite communication, in 1954. It seemed clear to me then, as it does now, that the best justification for developing communication satellites would be the linking together of the common-carrier communication systems of various continents. This would, for example, make the 46 million telephones of Europe (I use today's figures) more readily and more quickly accessible to the 83 million telephones of North America.

To broadcast directly to home receivers would necessitate putting heavy, high-powered, complicated equipment in a satellite, but my calculations showed that equipment of very low power could provide for the present rapid growth of international telephone and data transmission and, for the first time, link together the television networks of various continents.

In 1954 I was worried about problems of the life and reliability of any equipment launched into orbit, and I was encouraged to find that it would be possible to relay telephone and television signals by means of a passive, spherical, reflecting satellite. Indeed, for some of my calculations the model was a reflecting sphere 100 feet in diameter, and that is the very diameter of the Echo I balloon satellite which was launched into orbit on August 12, 1960.

Thus, Clarke proposed one thing in 1945 and I had something rather different in mind in 1954, which I published in 1955.[2] Something very close to the satellite I described was launched in 1960. Was this a direct result of my 1955 paper?

Oddly enough, the Echo balloon satellite itself was the result of work of a quite different character and purpose. In January, 1956, William J. O'Sullivan of the Langley Research Laboratory of the National Advisory Committee for Aeronautics, now incorporated in the National Aeronautics and Space Administration, proposed to launch balloon satellites in order to measure the density of the very tenuous atmosphere at an altitude of around 1,000 miles. His work led to the construction of an experimental 100-foot aluminized balloon.

After the launching of Sputnik late in 1957 and of Explorer I early in 1958, Rudolph Kompfner and I became very much concerned about a practical communication-satellite experiment. We saw in O'Sullivan's balloon the very object I had thought of in 1954 as a communication satellite. Our discussions with NASA led to their Echo program by early 1959. The plan was this. NASA would launch a 100-foot balloon satellite, for measuring atmospheric density *and* for communication. The Bell Telephone Laboratories would construct an East Coast communication terminal at Crawford Hill in New Jersey, and NASA's Jet Propulsion Laboratory would construct a communication terminal at Goldstone, California. All this was done, and President Eisenhower's spoken message was sent coast-to-coast by way of Echo on August 12, 1960.

Let me note briefly that the density of the atmosphere was duly derived from the orbital behavior of Echo I. R. W. Bryant[3] observes: "It must be pointed out in considering these density values that the atmosphere cannot be considered static at high altitudes. The diurnal effect can produce changes in density of as much as a factor of 30, and the effects associated with solar activity can produce changes of as much as a factor of 4 and possibly much greater. The seasonal effect may be as much as a factor of 1.5."

Let us return, however, to Echo I as a communication experiment. One important problem in carrying out such an experiment was that of pointing the transmitting and receiving antennas at the satellite. This could easily be done visually at night during clear weather when the satellite was in sunlight, but these qualifications are severe limitations. The satellite could be tracked by radar. But Newton's laws of motion and gravitation, which enabled Halley to predict the return in 1757 of the comet of 1682, which now bears his name, would make it possible to predict, from data acquired at one time, exactly where the antennas used in the communication experiment should be pointed at another time. Moreover, by using modern electronic gear, the antennas could be made to track the satellite automatically on the basis of the predicted position.

In project Echo, the existing minitrack network was the chief source of orbital information as long as the 108-megacycle beacon on the satellite remained active. Optical data from the Smithsonian Astrophysical Observatory were also used. Radar data from the West Coast communication terminal of the Jet Propulsion Laboratory at Goldstone were available during 1960.

In tracking Echo, orbital elements were computed by NASA's Goddard Space Flight Center at Greenbelt, Maryland. From these, elevation and rate of change of elevation and also azimuth and rate of change of azimuth were computed for times 4 seconds apart for each pass. To each such set of four data the time was added, and all the data for a pass were punched on a standard teletypewriter tape. Such tapes were transmitted to Holmdel (New Jersey), Goldstone, and other locations by commercial teletypewriter circuits. At Holmdel, the received tape was put into a digital-to-analog converter. When the clock time coincided with the time written on the tape, the angles and rates of change were automatically read out, converted to analog form, and used to drive the transmitting and receiving antennas.

In the Echo experiment this pointing was accurate to ±0.2 degree under favorable conditions. Such accuracy was not sufficient for TELSTAR, because the beam width of the Andover antenna is only 0.2 degree. At the TELSTAR ground terminal at Andover, Maine, a precision tracking antenna, operating on a 4,000-megacycle signal radiated by the satellite, supplies data from which orbital elements are computed. It was predicted—and the prediction has been borne out—that data from as few as two successive passes per day would make it possible to predict pointing angles with an accuracy of 0.02 degree for the subsequent 24 hours.

Programs for computing orbital elements and tracking data have been written for both the I.B.M. 7090 computers at the Bell Laboratories' Murray Hill and Whippany, New Jersey, locations, and for the two I.B.M. 1620 computers at Andover, Maine. The I.B.M. 7090 makes an orbital determination in a few minutes; the I.B.M. 1620's require about an hour and a half to process the data recorded during a pass, but they can handle data for three satellites in orbit.

We have seen how O'Sullivan's interest in the density of the exosphere was an important factor in the development of satellite communication. We see that the existence of electronic digital computers was essential in bridging the gap between Newton's laws and observations of the positions of Echo I and TELSTAR I, so that orbital computations could be made in minutes instead of months. As a communications engineer I do, however, propose to say *something* about electrical communication.

One of the great challenges of the Echo experiment was the fact that the 100-foot balloon reflected into the receiving antenna only about a millionth of a millionth of a millionth (10^{-18}) of the 10 kilowatts beamed at it by the transmitting antenna. The very low signal power received had to compete with noise from various sources. When I first considered satellite communication in 1954, by far the greatest source of such noise was the microwave receiver itself. I assumed that the receiver would introduce a noise equivalent to the Johnson or thermal noise of a body at a temperature of about 900 degrees Kelvin.

Happily, by the time the Echo experiment was carried out, matters had changed drastically. As a result of his studies in microwave spectroscopy after World War II, Townes invented the ammonia maser in 1954. This was followed by the invention of the three-level solid-state maser by Bloembergen, and by the time Project Echo was carried out, it was possible to use as an amplifier a maser which introduced a noise corresponding to the electromagnetic radiation from a body at a temperature of 8 degrees Kelvin, an improvement by a factor of 100 over the receiver I had visualized in 1954.

What would be the advantage of using such a receiver? This would depend on how much noise reached the receiver from the antenna. In 1954 this would have been negligible in comparison with the 900-degree noise temperature of a microwave receiver; in the Echo experiment it could be crucial in comparison with the 8-degree noise temperature of the maser.

The first requirement was that the antenna face the cool sky instead of the warm earth. Antennas with conventional dish-shaped parabolic reflectors "see" something of the environment to the sides and behind as well as in the direction in which they are pointed. Fortunately, in 1951, Friis and Beck[4] had described a "horn-reflector" antenna which is insensitive to radiation from the sides and back.

Let us suppose the antenna saw only the sky; what noise would be received? If the air were perfectly transparent, only noise from space. But, because air is not perfectly transparent, some thermal radiation must be received from it.

In 1947, Van Vleck gave formulas for the absorption of micro-waves by oxygen and water vapor. Using these, together with con-stants which had been determined experimentally and data concern-ing the density and temperature of the atmosphere, D. C. Hogg was able to compute the thermal noise which should be received at var-ious angles from the zenith as a function of receiver frequency.

However, his values still had to be verified experimentally. By September of 1959 this had been done with a maser and a small horn-reflector antenna. There was a close agreement between the theoretical and the experimental values.

There were, however, other sources of noise: thermal noise due to the rain, and scattering into the receiving antenna, by the rain, of energy from a microwave transmitter 20 miles away.

The maser was instrumental to the success of Echo and later of TELSTAR. The sensitivity of the maser made an investigation of sky noise imperative. For this, the horn-reflector antenna was called into use. And the results of the investigation indicated that gains could be made through the use of this type of antenna. Thus, for the Echo experiment, a horn-reflector antenna with an aperture of 400 square feet was constructed at Holmdel, and later a 3,600-square-foot antenna was constructed at Andover for the TELSTAR experi-ment.

The construction of such large antennas led to the problem of boresighting—that is, of determining just where the antenna beam is pointed for various mechanical positions of the structure. This is no easy problem for a large antenna. The electromagnetic point source which is used must lie outside Fresnel zone; this means that it must be at a distance greater than D^2/λ, where D is the diameter of the antenna aperture and λ is the wavelength. Thus, for an antenna 70 feet in diameter and a wavelength of $1/6$ foot (a frequency of 6,000 megacycles), the source used in boresighting should be more than 3,000 feet away. Airplanes and helicopters come to mind, but they are expensive and cumbersome for boresighting.

Happily, radio astronomy has provided us with the locations of a number of sufficiently distant radio sources, which have been identified with optically observed celestial objects. Some of the stronger sources are α Cassiopeiae, α Cygni, α Tauri, and α Virginis. Each of these sources can provide a number of data points as it moves across the sky. In particular, it is very useful to include at least one whose declination is approximately equal to the observer's, for it will then pass very near the zenith and thus become a sensitive indicator for azimuth boresighting.

Early in 1962 the antenna at Holmdel was boresighted by means of stellar radio sources. The tracking equipment was supplied with digital-computer data which would cause it to point exactly at a star and track it if the electrical and mechanical axes of the antenna were exactly aligned. A boresighting correction was obtained by offsetting the antenna in alternate senses by amounts that would reduce the output to a particular chosen value; the true direction of the source was taken as halfway between such offsets in azimuth and elevation. The root-mean-square scatter of the data was 0.01 degree in elevation and 0.025 degree in azimuth. The beam width at 2,390 megacycles is 1.4 degrees, so pointing errors could be determined to within 1/60 or less of the beam width.

The Andover antenna was boresighted by the same method.

It seems only fair that we communications engineers should try to repay our debt to radio astronomy. At present, A. A. Penzias is working to set a meaningful upper limit to the abundance in space of the OH radical, which has a spectral line at 1,677.34 megacycles. The sensitivity of the Holmdel receiver is such that results obtained with it should be more accurate than published results by two orders of magnitude.

Navigation, geodesy, and chronometry were once near the heart of astronomy, and TELSTAR I has made its contribution in this field.

On August 25 and 27, 1962, William Markowitz and C. A. Lidback of the U.S. Naval Observatory cooperated with J. M. Steele of the National Physical Laboratory, who suggested the experiment, in relating, to an unprecendented degree of accuracy, the master clocks of the Naval Observatory at Washington and the Royal Greenwich Observatory at Hurstmonceux. This was done by transmitting pulses from the ground stations at Andover, Maine, and at Goonhilly, Cornwall. The difference between time of reception and time of transmission of the pulses was measured at each station.

In addition, the Goonhilly station measured the time of arrival of its own pulses as transmitted by the Andover station. These data furnished both the difference between the clocks, as represented by the two pulsers, and the travel time. The difference between the Andover and Goonhilly clocks was determined to 1 microsecond. This represents nearly a thousand-fold improvement in accuracy of synchronization over the result of previous radio transmissions. The clocks at Washington and Hurstmonceux had been related to the Andover and Goonhilly clocks, respectively, to within about 10 microseconds; they can now be related to within 1 microsecond.

The measurements also gave a check on the accuracy of the orbital data; the ephemeris range was found to be accurate to about 1 kilometer.

I now turn to another topic of considerable interest to science. Prior to the launching of TELSTAR, in July 1962, our knowledge of the spectrum of electron and proton radiation in the Van Allen belt was meager, and we had little knowledge of how this radiation changed with time. Fortunately, a long program concerned with radiation damage to semiconductors and a small but active interest in low-energy nuclear physics had led to the development, from semiconductors, of particle detectors of great simplicity and accuracy. TELSTAR I was equipped with such detectors. Such detectors have been flown in the Injun and TRAAC satellites and in several Air Force satellites in the past two years, but little information is yet available from these experiments.

The detectors are p-n junction devices which, in effect, are small solid-state ionization chambers.[5] They give output pulses proportional to the energy deposited by an incident-charged particle in a disk-shaped active volume a few millimeters in diameter and a few tenths of a millimeter thick. This kind of device has been extensively used in low-energy nuclear physics experiments in the last several years and provides high energy-resolution and relatively high speed. In the TELSTAR experiment the devices were not used as high-resolution devices or at their maximum speed; nevertheless, the experience gained from the nuclear physics experiments with these devices was invaluable in designing the satellite experiment.

Three detectors measure protons in energy regions between 2.8 and 25 MeV, between 26 and 34 MeV, and above 50 MeV. The peak flux of the highest-energy protons in the inner Van Allen belt is very close to the figure given by Van Allen in 1959,[6] and the flux of lower-energy protons rises steeply, as had been observed at low altitudes by Naugle and Fichtel.[7] Quite comprehensive maps of these particles have been made over the range of TELSTAR's orbit. Protons are responsible for a major part of the radiation damage on the TELSTAR solar power plant; the damage would be much more serious were it not for the relatively thick sapphire shielding of the solar cells.

A fourth particle detector made from a semiconductor is used in studying the distribution of electrons in the trapped radiation belts. In this case particle pulses are introduced into four pulse-height channels below 1 MeV. Because of the nature of the processes of electron energy loss, the detector is also sensitive to electrons of higher energy.

Initially, the electron flux measured by TELSTAR I was about 10 times as great as had been expected, and the electron energy was considerably greater than had been expected. This is generally attributed to the high-altitude detonation of a nuclear device in the megaton yield range in the Pacific the day before TELSTAR was launched.

The unexpectedly high radiation measured by TELSTAR, and measured at lower altitudes by the Injun satellite, caused considerable scientific excitement. On October 27, NASA launched the Explorer XV radiation-measuring satellite. Despite the fact that the de-spin mechanism failed, this satellite has provided valuable data on the Van Allen belt and has added to our knowledge of the way the belt changes with time.

The radiation measured by TELSTAR I was unexpectedly high. So was the public excitement engendered by the first and by subsequent real-time transatlantic television programs which TELSTAR

I made possible. A United States Information Agency poll showed that in the week after the transatlantic television ceremonies of July 23, 1962, 82 percent of the people of Great Britain were able to identify the TELSTAR satellite by name, 79 percent knew it was a United States achievement, and 59 percent saw the television program beamed from the United States. In a message broadcast to the people of the Commonwealth, Christmas Day, 1962, Queen Elizabeth referred to TELSTAR as "the invisible focus of a million eyes," and used this new star to draw man's attention to the star the Wise Men of old followed, and to its message.

TELSTAR was an engineering experiment which took us a step forward in understanding and capability. The interest excited by TELSTAR made people want to know when satellites would become a regularly functioning part of the world's communication network, what sort of satellites would be used, and how a satellite communication system would be brought into being.

When work was started toward developing an experimental active communication satellite in the research department of the Bell Telephone Laboratories late in 1959, we had great enthusiasm for a proposed 24-hour synchronous satellite which would hang stationary above a spot on the equator at an altitude of 22,300 miles. We realized, however, that the time delay in transmission might seriously impair the usefulness of such a satellite for telephony.

While long-distance or trunk telephone circuits use separate paths in the two directions, the circuits from switching offices to subscribers send signals both ways over the same pair of wires. Devices called hybrid coils are used to attain some degree of independence of transmission in the two directions. Nonetheless, all the world's 140 million telephones reflect a small percentage of energy directed toward them. When the person on the phone hears this reflected speech delayed by 0.1 second or more he finds it unpleasant and upsetting. Thus, echo suppressors are inserted at the ends of trunk circuits longer than 1,500 miles. These devices turn off the outward path when a signal is present on the inward path. Provision is made for breaking in by talking very loudly.

Echo suppressors are tolerable for handling echo delays encountered in continental telephony and even in transoceanic telephony by way of submarine cable. Would they be tolerable for an echo delayed 0.6 second, as would be the case in talking by way of a synchronous satellite?

This is no easy matter to decide, for the answer could depend on the people involved, on the nature of the conversation, and perhaps on the design of the echo suppressor. Psychologists have been studying this problem at the Bell Laboratories for over two years. As in the case of most experiments, answering one question raises another. However, we hope to have some convincing numerical data within a few months. At present I can only say that, under realistic conditions, a delay of 0.6 second, even when the best echo suppressors available are used, proves unacceptable in a substantial percentage of conversations.

This result seemingly flies in the face of the fact that laboratory workers often feel, after casual trials, that a circuit with echo suppressors which has a delay of 0.6 second is quite satisfactory. It is here that we see the difference between experimental science as we know it in our time and the sort of casual experience which was man's sole and inadequate guide in earlier ages.

In citing this example of human response to a communication system I have strayed from physics, but I have not departed from the realm of science and technology. Satellite communication itself has stirred other realms. I think I scarcely need describe the somewhat heady, or perhaps I should say dizzy, feeling I had during a period when the President of the United States and members of Congress proposed and discussed legislation engendered by the existence of a communication satellite, a satellite whose very existence depended in part on earlier work of mine. Perhaps the dizziness was caused by the stupendous gulf, physical and otherwise, which separated me from the political scene: I followed events in the newspapers, but I had no direct part in them.

On August 31, 1962, President Kennedy signed a Communications Satellite Act which, after long hearings and much debate and amendment, had passed both houses of Congress. This act sets the pattern for United States participation in any international civilian satellite communication system. The exclusive right is granted to a new corporation created by law for this single purpose.

Traditionally, the communication common carriers have had freedom to use directly, as a part of their very diverse communication facilities, any part of the science and technology which has come to them from so many sources. Thus, their facilities have come to include wire, cable, coaxial cable, submarine cable, short-wave radio, ultrahigh-frequency radio, tropospheric scatter, and microwave radio relay systems.

The Communications Satellite Act and the entirely new corporation which it has created represent a bold venture into completely uncharted waters. Its activities are confined to one particular aspect of common-carrier communication—supplying circuits by means of satellites. The stock is to be owned partly by the general public and partly by communication common carriers. The board of directors is to have members representing the noncommunication investors, who presumably want to make money; the common carriers, who urgently need more transoceanic circuits, whether these be supplied by cables or by satellites; and members appointed by the President, who has strongly asserted that satellite communication should serve the needs of the inhabitants of the least developed areas of the globe. For this new and unique corporation to act successfully in establishing the necessary research and development resources for reaching its various goals in a tricky and scarcely tried field of technology will require unprecedented pluck and ingenuity.

I began by proclaiming myself no historian, and I am certainly no prophet. In closing, let me return to the things I have observed over the few years of my life that have been devoted in part to communication satellites.

I think that the relations I have pointed out between the work on Echo I and TELSTAR I and work in the fields of upper-atmosphere physics, celestial mechanics, electronic computers, molecular spectroscopy and masers, radio astronomy, and experimental psychology aptly illustrate the fact that the science and technology involved in any complicated undertaking come from so many sources that no one can call them his own. Science and technology belong to no enterprise and to no nation; they are part of the heritage and the work of men throughout the world. Governments and other institutions may support, license, forbid, and enforce conformity, but they can neither legislate the laws of nature out of existence nor prevent men outside of their area of control from discovering and using them.

But the powers that governments exercise can have drastic effects, both on the lives and work of scientists and engineers and on the degree of benefit that society reaps from science and technology. And these powers are as often exercised foolishly and ignorantly as with informed wisdom.

C. P. Snow has spoken of two worlds in modern society—the world of polite learning and the world of science and technology. I myself find a more real distinction between two other worlds. These two worlds can exist even in the thought and action of one individual, though perhaps they more often manifest themselves separately: one in an engineer; the other in a statesman or a religious leader.

One of these worlds has two aspects: it is the world of natural law and of the understanding and application of natural law which are expressed in our science and technology. Some things are possible; some are beyond possibility. At a given time we can in part distinguish between the possible and the impossible. Of those things which are possible, some we can this very day achieve by an effort commensurate with their value. Some we can have, but at far too dear a price. Some, though possible in principle, are beyond our present grasp, however hard we may strive.

This world of our understanding of nature and the power that it gives us varies not only with time but among individuals and institutions. What one can do is beyond the grasp of another. Yet, whatever ephemeral and elusive qualities this world of science and technology may appear to have, it is exceedingly powerful, though extremely obdurate. The possibilities of great things are within our grasp, and men and institutions exist by means of which these great things can be accomplished.

The other world is, let us say, a personal world, the world of our aspirations—of our needs, desires, dislikes, and hates. It is the world of what we would like to accomplish and of how we would prefer to achieve it. The obdurate world of science and technology can sometimes help us to distinguish wishful thinking from what is possible, of fantasy from what will work. It can sometimes enable us to foretell otherwise unexpected and unpleasant consequences of capricious behavior.

Projects and people succeed in the degree that their aspirations are wise and realistic. I believe that our knowledge of the powerful but obdurate world of science and technology can add wisdom and realism to our world of personal and national conduct. But I believe that too, too often men and nations expect the laws of nature, the state of technology, and the abilities of people and of institutions to conform to their aspirations, instead of making their aspirations conform to the obdurate world of science and technology.

NOTES

[1] A. C. Clarke, *Wireless World,* Vol. LI, No. 305 (October, 1945).

[2] J. R. Pierce, *Jet Propulsion,* Vol. XXV, No. 153 (April, 1955).

[3] R. W. Bryant, "A Comparison of Theory and Observation of the Echo Satellite," *NASA Technical Note D-1124* (1961).

[4] H. T. Friis and A. C. Beck, U.S. Patent No. 2,236,393, issued March 25, 1941.

[5] W. L. Brown, *IRE Transactions on Nuclear Science,* Vol. VIII, No. 2 (1961).

[6] J. A. Van Allen, *Journal of Geophysical Research,* Vol. LXIV, No. 1683 (1959).

[7] J. E. Naugle and C. E. Fichtel, *Bulletin of the American Physical Society,* Vol. VI, No. 53 (1961).

The Beginning and End of an Era in Satellite Communication*

TODAY we are faced with entirely new potentialities in satellite communication. Both the space art and the electronic art have advanced more rapidly than I would have dared to dream in the days of the Echo and TELSTAR satellites. Today the Titan III-C booster makes it possible to launch a satellite weighing a ton into synchronous orbit. Solid-state electronics and integrated circuits have so far advanced that such a satellite could provide reliably and economically a communication capacity of 100,000 two-way telephone circuits, for telephone transmission and such other uses as television and data, among five or ten principal cities in the United States. Such a satellite system could be established in a few years, and in this short time it could substantially increase the number of long-distance circuits available. Further, in concert with terrestrial facilities, the satellite could incorporate switching equipment which would transfer blocks of circuits from one pair of cities to another in meeting fluctuations in demand.

Such a capability does not change former concepts, it makes them obsolete. By comparison, proposals for special-purpose domestic satellite systems seem as modern as antimacassars. If we are wise and energetic we can ultimately distribute transmission and switching functions optimally in an integrated satellite and land network of which every element is built and functions as part of one overall design. There are no limits on the future.

In some ways the new problems we face today remind me of our problems in the days before the Echo and TELSTAR satellites. Today, as then, we have enthusiastic people who want to try the wrong thing at the wrong time. Today, as then, we have the lethargy

* From a talk delivered at the University of California, January, 1967

and diverse purposes of agencies public and private. But there are differences. Today our technology is more assured, but public interest and disagreement are greater, so that it is harder to move forward. And today we have both a Communications Satellite Corporation which operates with a consortium of foreign agencies in providing foreign communication via satellites, and domestic common carriers whose purpose is to provide domestic communication by the most economical means available.

The future is more complicated than the past. And the future is yet to unfold. We are at the end of a brief era, and at the beginning of another. If we cannot see forward into the future, it is at least appropriate to look backward and discover the past.

Arthur C. Clarke first proposed satellite communication in an article published in the *Wireless World* in October, 1945. By 1954 the general idea of satellite communication was in the air. When, as a science fiction fan and writer, I was asked to talk to the Princeton Section of the Institute of Radio Engineers on October 14, 1954, I chose Orbital Radio Relays as a topic.

In 1954 and 1955 I thought: "There is little reason to believe that a satellite relay could compete with present microwave radio relay or coaxial cable in cost." Here I was clearly too conservative. But could I have known how rapid progress would be?

In the summer of 1958, Rudolph Kompfner and I attended a meeting on communication held at Woods Hole under Air Force sponsorship. There a number of eager proponents discussed satellite communication. One proposal was for an active satellite with a powerful transmitter—using a traveling-wave tube that had a life of only 200 hours! Another proposal was for a low-altitude satellite with a tape recorder, to record and retransmit messages. I believe that this was then called Mailbag. Such a satellite, called Courier, was finally launched on October 4, 1960. This complex satellite failed after 17 days.

Kompfner and I felt little would be accomplished in a satellite communication experiment unless it succeeded, and that an experiment with a passive balloon satellite would be challenging and feasible.

In January, 1956, William J. O'Sullivan of the Langley Research Laboratory of the National Advisory Committee for Aeronautics, now incorporated in the National Aeronautics and Space Administration, had proposed to launch balloon satellites in order to measure the density of the very tenuous atmosphere.

William H. Pickering, the head of the Jet Propulsion Laboratory, agreed that an experiment with O'Sullivan's balloon would be a profitable one, and offered his encouragement and support.

In order to convince ourselves and others of the value of such a passive satellite experiment, Kompfner and I wrote a paper, "Transoceanic Communication by Means of Satellites," which I delivered at the National Symposium on Extended Range Communications, held at the Lisner Auditorium in Washington, D.C., October 6 and 7, 1958, and which was published in the March, 1959, issue of the *Proceedings of the Institute of Radio Engineers*.

We then presented communication calculations concerning a 100-foot-diameter balloon satellite, and pointed out the need for work on components for active satellites.

But there were more daring plans for satellite communication in those days. In October of 1958 I became a member of the Advanced Research Projects Agency Ad Hoc Panel for Communications Satellites. The Services briefed this panel, using glorious renditions in color of soldiers in foxholes holding walkie-talkie satellite terminals in their hands. Other Service "requirements" were somewhat more modest, but all were far beyond any art that had been demonstrated, and called for very complex equipment in the satellites. The source of this insanity was that uniformed but enthusiastic men had taken as their starting point *needs* rather than potentialities or opportunities.

In the face of such Service "requirements," ARPA would not support a simple passive satellite experiment. Perhaps ARPA overestimated the state of the art. The Army's Project Score satellite, launched on December 18, 1958, showed that communication via active satellite was possible. Score was a real milestone, but ARPA may have misread the distance. In any event, ARPA felt that the very first step must be a complete system meeting Service requirements.

Concentration on narrow and unreasonable "needs" often leads to stupendous but sterile efforts. Certainly, we feel the need for a cure for cancer, but we cannot solve this problem by following a typical military procurement routine. If we could, it would seem only reasonable to initiate, not only a project for the cure of cancer, but one for the elimination of death as well. Military procurement practices may be all right for producing old-fashioned things that have been made and evaluated before, but new things must begin, not with what we think we want, but with what new potentialities open up to us.

The outcome of ARPA's considerations was Project Advent. Advent was spelled out early in 1960. Advent was in effect abandoned early in 1962. The total expenditure had been around 170 million dollars. No satellites had been launched. Some ground terminals had been constructed, but these were perhaps less effective than those which were built and used in connection with the Echo I and TELSTAR satellites.

Advent was doomed from the start. In a paper, "The Illimitable Future of Satellite Communication," prepared for E. C. Welsh, Executive Secretary, National Aeronautics and Space Council, and sent to him on June 20, 1961, I wrote:

Advent illustrates some of the consequences of setting a goal far beyond the technical resources available. The goal of Advent has been a highly elaborate satellite communication system designed to meet detailed and stringent military requirements. This called for a very heavy payload in a 22,300-mile-high, 24-hour "stationary" orbit, with attitude control and station keeping. This went beyond existing or even nearly existing art in four respects (payload, orbit, attitude control, and station keeping). Indeed, the space art of 1962 can launch an experimental advent satellite only in an orbit much lower than that required for an operational system. In addition, Advent calls for very elaborate electronic equipment which, in view of the failure of Courier, might make one shudder even today. So far, none of the difficult features of Advent has been brought to test. Rather than having demonstrated a sequence of advances in the art, we face a day of reckoning with some foreboding.

I have also referred to a letter I wrote to L. C. Tillotson on August 26, 1959, in order to refresh my memory of an even earlier day. I find that I then thought that we could best work toward a reliable synchronous active satellite system quickly and with a high probability of success by bypassing problems of attitude control for a while and launching a suitable repeater in a 3,000-mile orbit, in order to test the repeater electronics and to gain experience. The letter was in response to Tillotson's suggestions concerning the construction and trial of an active satellite, work which led ultimately to the TELSTAR satellite.

Although Kompfner and I could find no enthusiasm for a passive satellite experiment in ARPA or in the Services, NASA was receptive. The 100-foot balloons built by William J. O'Sullivan for the measurement of atmospheric density seemed a proper tool for such an experiment. Early in 1959, NASA became convinced that such an experiment was indeed desirable. Project Echo was initiated.

In order for Project Echo to be undertaken, NASA had to commit itself to the construction and launching of a satellite, the Bell Laboratories had to commit itself to the building of ground communication equipment, and the Jet Propulsion Laboratory also had to commit itself to building ground communication equipment. All these commitments were based on a general sort of need. But chiefly, they were based on exploiting the potentialities of what we believed to be current art, including some which had not been tried and applied.

On the basis of the existing art and alternative modes of communication, we knew that Echo was an experiment and that it would not satisfy any particular operating criterion. Echo could be only a step, but if it succeeded it would be a step in the right direction. NASA's was the greatest commitment to the experiment, and it surely required courage to undertake a communications experiment that would be of no operational use. The Jet Propulsion Laboratory also bore a heavy burden. Financially, our commitment at the Bell Laboratories was less than NASA's, but we undertook the commitment with our eyes open, realizing that what we were buying was not communication, but knowledge and experience.

Before even the general form of the Echo project could be decided upon, we had many informal discussions of technological resources and of what old and new devices and techniques were available. These were carried out at the Bell Laboratories by Kompfner, a few other people, and I, long before any organization was set up. This was necessary so that we would know how an organization could be adapted to the needs of the project, and so that it would have something to do.

We had to consider not only the inanimate resources, but also the human resources of the Bell Laboratories. Only certain people in the research department and outside were capable of doing some of the things that would have to be done. We had to talk to these people and get commitments from them. In case they were outside the research department, they or we had to convince their organizations as well as themselves, so that they would and could assume the burden of particular jobs.

Thus, by the time we came to worry about an organization, we had a fairly clear idea of our technical and human resources and of the problems that had to be solved. In fact, the organization was pretty well taken care of except for one thing—a project engineer. It was his responsibility to understand the project as a whole, to inform himself of the progress of the various workers, to deal with NASA and the Jet Propulsion Laboratory and the aspects of the project which were not ours, to arrange special and periodic meetings, and to keep a record of the progress of the project.

William C. Jakes undertook this responsibility. Organizationally, Jakes reported to A. B. Crawford, who reported to Kompfner and Cutler, the director and assistant director of radio and electronics research, who in turn reported to me. Many of the 20 or 30 people who worked full time on the project were organizationally on the same level as Jakes, and some who played a very active part were one or two levels higher. The responsibility, however, was Jakes's. No one else at any time so much as thought of making any change in the project or its activities except through Jakes, and it was Jakes's responsibility to ask for any help he needed in reaching decisions. This organization, if organization it was, worked admirably right to the final moment of communicating by means of Echo, when, on Jakes's orders, Kompfner and I, along with all other nonoperating personnel, left the control building a half hour before the satellite appeared over the horizon.

As far as I can see, the approach that we used at the Bell Laboratories in connection with Project Echo was admirably suited to research of a systems nature. People in other parts of the company, as well as the research department, worked in an orderly, timely fashion on the various aspects of Echo, and they stayed in their permanent organizational position, reporting to their supervision. On the other hand, no one questioned the fact that everything had to be done with the agreement of Jakes, for he was responsible for seeing that everything was completed and functioned together on time. In this he exercised whatever authority his supervision had, right to the top. When the project was over, various people went back to other work as their services were no longer needed, and their relationship with Jakes automatically vanished.

Prior to the launching of Echo, the transmitting, receiving, and tracking equipment at Crawford Hill and Goldstone was exercised by bouncing signals off the Moon, during the period from November 23, 1959, through August 7, 1960. Signals were bounced off Tiros on May 5, May 11, and July 29, 1960. Before the Echo launch, NASA conducted several suborbital "Shotput" launches from Wallops Island, Virginia. On those of January 16 and February 27, 1960, signals were sent via the balloon from Crawford Hill to a receiver at the Lincoln Laboratory station at Round Hill, Massachusetts.

Echo I was successfully launched on August 12, 1960, and on the very first pass President Eisenhower's spoken message was sent coast-to-coast from Goldstone to Crawford Hill.

We were gratified by the success of the Echo I experiment. Some consideration was given to pursuing it by constructing terminals capable of transmitting television via a somewhat larger balloon satellite. But by the end of 1959 our thoughts were definitely directed toward a simple, low-altitude active satellite as the next step toward a commercially useful satellite communication system. I felt at the time that such a satellite must be broadband enough to transmit television or hundreds of telephone channels if it was really to demonstrate useful performance, and that it must be a simple, low-power satellite if it was to achieve a useful reliability.

It is interesting to compare the satellite proposed by L. C. Tillotson in an internal memorandum dated August 24, 1959, with the TELSTAR satellite:

	Tillotson	TELSTAR
Output Power	1 watt	2 watts
RF Bandwidth	100 Mc	50 Mc
Frequency	6 kMc	6.39 kMc up
		4.17 kMc down
Diameter	4 feet	32 inches
Altitude	2,500 miles	512-3,043 nmi

The larger diameter of the satellite Tillotson proposed would have allowed continuous operation rather than the intermittent operation obtained in the TELSTAR satellite. Both satellites were roughly spherical, with equatorial antennas and spin orientation. Both the satellite proposed by Tillotson and the TELSTAR satellite used frequency conversion of the received signal to an IF frequency, up conversion and amplification by a traveling-wave tube. Wide deviation FM with an FM with feedback receiver on the ground was common to both.

Work was initiated in the research department, with help from various areas of the development departments, toward the satellite which Tillotson proposed. The work was necessarily carried on at a modest level, especially prior to the successful launching of Echo I on August 12, 1960. The success of Echo I generated such an enthusiasm inside and outside the Bell System as to speed technical progress toward an active satellite system. In the summer of 1960 the primary responsibility for carrying out an active satellite experiment was transferred to an organization in the development part of the Bell Laboratories, headed by A. C. Dickieson, and E. F. O'Neill became the project engineer responsible for the satellite which became TELSTAR.

One of the greatest problems proved to be that of finding a way to get an active satellite launched. To this end a group of Bell Laboratories people, including myself, visited NASA headquarters in Washington on November 4, 1960, and had a friendly meeting with Hugh L. Dryden, Robert C. Seamans, Leonard Jaffe, and others concerning the possibility of NASA's launching an experimental Bell System satellite. At this meeting we were told that NASA planned to contract for an experimental satellite (Relay), and we gathered that it would be a good idea to bid on Relay, even though the American Telephone and Telegraph Company was prepared to bear the cost of the satellite and the launching.

Various companies came forward with proposals for launching for a fee, but NASA really controlled the boosters. Thus, when a request for a proposal on Relay was finally received on January 4, 1961, AT&T decided to bid on it, even though this meant a substantial change in plans, including a change in frequency of operation.

AT&T put in its bid on Relay on March 20, 1961. But on May 18, 1961, it was announced that the contract had gone to RCA. This meant two things—reverting to the original frequencies of operation, and searching for a means of launching the satellite. We searched desperately. It proved impractical to have the satellite launched by the Armed Forces. Our mood was such that Kompfner and I jokingly asked a visiting Soviet scientist[1] whether we might not get a Russian rocket. He said this was impractical when he could not even buy a skindiving outfit in this country and take it back to the Soviet Union.

On July 27, 1961, NASA finally agreed to supply AT&T with a booster; the price was 3.5 million dollars per launch, a license under all Bell System patents in the satellite field, and a right to license anyone else under these patents. Thus, AT&T was able to proceed with its TELSTAR program, but very late and, seemingly, at great potential cost in the field of patents.

The TELSTAR project was huge compared with Echo, and the Bell Laboratories was responsible for the satellite as well as the terminals. At the peak of activity, some 500 people were involved full time.

The first TELSTAR satellite was successfully launched on July 10, 1962, less than two months before the Communications Satellite Act made it impossible for AT&T to proceed toward a commercial satellite communication system for foreign communication.

The TELSTAR satellite was a popular and technical success, even though it soon lost its intended meaning as a step toward an early establishment of international commercial service.

NASA's Relay satellite was launched on December 13, 1962. Relay has been a worthy experiment, but we have learned little from it that we did not know from the TELSTAR satellites. Syncom is a different story.

Syncom is the outcome of the bold and ingenious belief of a group of engineers at Hughes that one could make an extremely small but reliable synchronous satellite and successfully launch it with the rather small Thor-Delta vehicle used to launch such low-altitude satellites as Echo, TELSTAR, and Relay. Attitude control was merely by spinning, with an ingenious jet system for corrections of axis and position. No batteries were incorporated; the satellite operates only when in sunlight. Everything was cut to the bone. But, though the first launch on February 14, 1963, failed, Syncom II, launched July 26, 1963, and Syncom III, launched August 19, 1964, succeeded and have operated well ever since.

The success of Syncom makes one wonder why anyone was ever

interested in low-altitude satellites. When work was started toward developing an experimental active communication satellite in the research department of the Bell Telephone Laboratories late in 1959, we had great enthusiasm for a 24-hour synchronous satellite which would hang stationary about a spot on the equator at an altitude of 22,300 miles. We realized, however, that the time delay in transmission might seriously impair the usefulness of such a satellite for telephony.

Echo suppressors are tolerable for handling echo delays encountered in continental telephony and even in transoceanic telephony by way of submarine cable. Would they be tolerable for an echo delayed 0.6 second, as would be the case in talking by way of a synchronous satellite?

This is no easy matter to decide, for the answer could depend on the people involved, on the nature of the conversation, and perhaps on the design of the echo suppressor. Psychologists have been studying this problem at the Bell Laboratories for more than five years. As in the case of most experiments, answering one question raises another.

Tests are still going on. It appears that a round-trip delay as long as or even somewhat longer than that for a synchronous satellite does not in itself seriously impair communication. However, a substantial fraction of users find any two-wire circuit with this delay and with echo suppressors less satisfactory than a circuit with the delay characteristic of undersea cables. There seems to be little choice among existing echo suppressors; all interrupt the two-way connection, and that is what does the damage.

We hope that in the future it will be possible to cancel out echoes by means of an adaptive network; we have demonstrated this in the laboratory. When this proves practical, circuits provided by synchronous satellites will be comparable in quality to other circuits.

Score, Echo, TELSTAR, Relay, and Syncom were important experimental steps toward some sort of satellite communication system. With each, we either learned something, or became more sure in what we felt that we knew. In inception, these all belong to the period of aggressive technical progress which preceded the Communications Satellite Act.

Much of what happened thereafter had a strong flavor of requirements, paper studies, plans, and proposals which is reminiscent of the days preceding Advent. This was so in both civilian and military satellite communication. The story is admirably set forth in "Satellite Communications," an October, 1964, report of the House Military Operations Subcommittee, of which Congressman Chet Holifield of California is chairman. I have drawn heavily on this to supplement my personal knowledge of events.

On the civilian side, one of the earliest effects of the new communications satellite situation was to bring to an end one of the few areas of international, technical, nonpolitical, cooperative work which remained in this increasingly nationalistic world. International telecommunications had for many decades operated successfully through technological and commercial cooperation. The government-owned telephone and telegraph systems, together with their American privately owned counterparts, found quiet and satisfactory ways for bringing into being and operating international telephone and telegraph services. Discussions were chiefly between technical and operating personnel, though of course governments had to ratify international agreements.

Those days are gone forever. A strong nationalistic and political flavor now permeates all international telecommunications, but especially, all efforts toward satellite communications.

In the rest of the world, the organizations responsible for satellite communication are operating telecommunications agencies, technically and industrially powerful, though less powerful than those of the United States. These agencies are in the business of supplying complete telecommunications services both nationally and internationally with most nations of the world, including ours. They have knowledge, experience, powerful research laboratories, and an assured source of income, both from and for operations, and for research and development.

In this country, we have in the Communications Satellite Corporation a new company dedicated to the marketing, not of a complete communication service, but of a small and specialized part of a communication service: long-distance trunk circuits via satellite. These will at most form a link in various complicated communications paths. The company had no experience in the field of communication, no established research facilities, and no income. Except for service supplied to agencies of the government, it could derive income only by supplying service to foreign *as well as* American common carriers. This service supplements existing means of international communication.

In December, 1962, the telecommunications committee of the 22-nation European Conference of Postal and Telecommunication Administration (CEPT) set up a committee to study the problems posed by the entirely novel situation which the Communications Satellite Act had created. A series of meetings followed. These led to the formation of a Consortium, an international business-type financial pool, to deal with the Communications Satellite Corporation on behalf of member nations.

Negotiations with the Corporation led to an Interim Communications Satellite Committee, established formally on August 19, 1964. In this, the United States initially has 61 percent ownership, which could conceivably fall to 50.6 percent. This committee has the task of deciding on an international civilian satellite communication system and bringing it into being.

The Communications Satellite Corporation has the major ownership, and it nominally has the strongest voice in this undertaking. Against this are the facts that the various telecommunications administrations of the Consortium are experienced in the field of communications, have a going business, have some good research laboratories, and are in general technically strong.

In a practical way, this means that insofar as these foreign members of the Consortium are united, they are in a position to dictate to the Communications Satellite Corporation, which can either comply or have no business. This was clearly demonstrated when the Consortium refused to sanction a joint military and civilian system which the United States Department of Defense and the Communications Satellite Corporation proposed.

Cashing in on Syncom, the Communications Satellite Corporation launched an improved version of that satellite, called Early Bird, in 1965, and has launched other satellites since. Early Bird provides 240 two-way telephone circuits or one television channel between this country and Europe. Beyond this, the Corporation has let study contracts toward a later system.

The Department of Defense and the military Services have been technically much stronger and more experienced in communication than the Communications Satellite Corporation. The Services have some good research and development laboratories. They are more experienced in contracting. It is hard to see what the Department of Defense thought it could gain by working through the Communications Satellite Corporation as a sort of middleman—and in a plan that was sure to be unacceptable to foreign participants.

The only clear effect of the proposed joint civilian-military system was to interrupt progress toward a military satellite system for about a year.

The report of Congressman Holifield's subcommittee ascribes our halting progress toward a military system to timidity on the part of Secretary of Defense Robert S. McNamara. This seems an insufficient explanation, and there seems to be no explanation that is both credible and creditable.

When we look back at military space communication, we find that by 1954 the Naval Research Laboratory had transmitted a voice message over an Earth-Moon path. In 1959, the Navy established the first operational Moon link, between Washington, D.C., and Hawaii. The Services were slow in exploiting this potentially valuable form of communication. Following the success of Echo I in 1960, the Services could have exploited passive satellite communication, together with communication using the Moon as a reflector. But at that time the Services were hypnotized by the Advent chimera. The Advent chimera was dispelled by the "reorientation" of Advent in 1962. The Services then, sensibly but late, embarked on a conservative system, consistent with what the TELSTAR and Relay programs verified. But this program was delayed for about a year by the utterly silly idea of providing a joint civilian-military system through the Communications Satellite Corporation.

Today, seven IDCSP (Initial Defense Communication System Project) satellites have been launched in near-synchronous orbits, and other launchings are planned. These satellites are regarded as experimental, but provide some useful communication. Further, NASA has transferred Syncom II and Syncom III to the Defense Department. Thus, the Military have adequate means for gaining operational experience with satellite communication.

The prospects for military satellite communication are bright. There are many plausible uses for the sort of communication that satellites can supply, both now and in the future. In the Air Force Titan III-C we have the first booster which promises to be big enough, simple enough, reliable enough, and cheap enough for space projects which are useful (as is satellite communication) rather than merely adventurous. Finally, the Lincoln Laboratory, which is outstanding in experience and skill in the field of communication, has been given a mission in military satellite communication, is being funded on a continuing basis in that field, and has successfully launched several experimental satellites. In the military field, satellite work long went the dreary rounds of studies and contracts. I believe that the Lincoln Laboratory can play an essential and indispensable part in the realization and advance of satellite communication.

For a considerable time the prospects of civilian satellite communication seemed far drearier. The Communications Satellite Corporation has no resource such as the Lincoln Laboratory. It must contract for research and development. Experience has shown that research and development by contract can be effective, but are slow and expensive, and therefore dubious in an undertaking which must make a profit. European telecommunications agencies have tended to abandon limited contracts with competitive bidding in favor of long-term contracts covering a field. Even such contracts are at a disadvantage compared with in-house capability.

All this is, however, the pattern of the past. As I noted above, revolutionary technological progress in two powerful fields—communication and space—has made our initial conception of satellite communication as dated as the dodo. I was too shortsighted to see what was coming. So were others. Our government planned and legislated for the past instead of for the future.

What the future can bring is immeasurably good. Surely, what it will bring must be far beyond what we have now. It is only reasonable to expect that we will make mistakes comparable to or greater than those of the past. But our accomplishments will be greater, too.

NOTE

[1] Z. S. Chernov of the Lebedev Institute, who visited the Bell Laboratories in April, 1961.

III
Science, Scientists, and Society

Scientists and engineers are people in the real world, but their lives, problems, and influences are in some ways special.

The Social Uses of Science*

RECENTLY, a publisher suggested that I write a book about cybernetics, automatic machines, and thinking machines, and about the effect that all these may have on society. As he outlined what he had in mind (leaving examples and words to me), I felt that this was not the sort of book which is needed. I found his ideas fantastic and misleading, yet clearly he felt that this was what the public wanted to read about science, and it was equally clear that he would find someone to write the volume.

There is no lack of books which describe the wonders of science as seen from the outside looking in, of books which speculate on what science may do to society, and of books whose authors, seemingly at least, abstract facts or principles from science to guide man in other fields of endeavor. In the face of this one-sided plethora, perhaps it is worth while to look from science out on the uses of science and of the concepts of science in our own society, right in the present.

Such a look should embrace more than books, but books are a natural starting point, and especially books on philosophy. Not long ago I had the amusing experience of glancing through a book on Soviet philosophy. Here, at a time when Western philosophers quote relativity and quantum mechanics, was a philosophy ostensibly based on the work of Newton, Laplace, and Lagrange. It was refreshing to find this science, still as valid as ever and so much more familiar to me than relativity and quantum mechanics, used in a modern philosophical work. I cannot say, however, that the conclusions drawn by the Soviet philosopher seemed as clear and as reliable as the science on which they were said to be based.

The same science on which all in the laboratory agree appears to

* Reprinted with permission from *American Scientist*, Vol. 42, No. 4 (October, 1954), 646–650; copyright © 1954, by the Society of the Sigma Xi.

lead philosophers in different directions. Henry Adams made use of Gibbs's thermodynamics and statistical mechanics, which are perfectly consistent with classical physics, as a basis for a philosophy of history with which the Russians surely would not agree. Others than professional philosophers have used science to reach a surprising diversity of views. Scientists themselves, wearied with their inching progress from the unknown to the known, are continually tempted into amateur philosophizing, seeking—always just beyond what is firmly in their grasp—some ultimate light on the nature of man or of the universe. This leads, year by year, to various elucidations of the relations between relativity and morals and between the uncertainty principle and free will. It also gives us charming and imaginative popular accounts of the origin of the universe, of the solar system, and of life itself.

The use of science in philosophy is fascinating, but it is puzzling as well. An engineer uses science in a direct way; he makes use on a large and purposeful scale of certain natural phenomena with which science has acquainted him and over which science has given him control. The use of science in philosophy is different, and to distinguish this we might call it a *social* use. A mob might make a similar social use of religion in justifying the burning of an unpopular citizen; this should be contrasted with the uses made of religion by a mystic, a saint, or even an everyday good man. Strangers make a similar social use of music, or art, or literature as alternatives to the weather in polite conversation; we may contrast this with the enjoyment or creation of actual music, pictures, or books.

In the social use of science by philosophers, science is used as a whole or in part as an authority and example: to be attacked, to be upheld, or to be cited as a basis for belief. For the engineer's use, science must be correct, just as for the music lover music must be enjoyable. If we replaced the engineer's exact textbooks with books full of errors, he would be unable to make workable devices. In the social uses of science it is prestige which is important, not truth or falsity. Indeed, in most social uses, the newest, the most tentative, and the most dubious parts of science are those most often relied on.

Once the use of science in philosophy is recognized as a purely social use, unconnected with the scientific or engineering uses of science, and not dependent on the verity of science, it is easy to find social uses of science in other fields.

When science is used in philosophy, it is not always used as a source of authority; sometimes it is decried or berated. Outside the groves of academe, science is an authority which it is difficult to challenge on other grounds. Advertisements, for instance, do not generally recommend cigarettes or deodorants as religiously approved or as patriotic; they recommend them in the name of science.

As in the case of philosophy, in the social use of science as authority the appeal is not to science in any narrow, understood, and verifiable form, but to science in the distant large. In any particular instance, people feel free to choose what they will or will not believe, quite independently of what science may have to say.

An engineer friend of mine chanced on a man vainly trying to siphon water over a hill somewhat more than thirty feet high. That water is supported in a siphon by air pressure is a scientific fact, as true now as it was when discovered in the seventeenth century. My friend advised the man that water can rise in a siphon only a little over thirty feet. The man replied, "You can pull the water up as far as you want if you have suck enough," and he went on pumping. The authority of science was at nought in this particular instance, and the man retained his fixed idea in the face of his own contrary experience.

The case of a checker-playing machine, considerably discussed in the press, is quite different. A mathematician, a friend of mine, was skeptical and inquired into the matter. The maker of the machine readily admitted it to be a hoax. "But you are the first person who doubted it," he said.

In one instance, a man disregarded both the authority of science and his own experience. In the other, a large number of people were quite willing to believe that a fantastic machine had been built, in the light of no personal experience whatever, and probably through a misunderstanding of what some popular writer had stated.

This should not astound us. The social use of science as an authority has undoubtedly arisen because of the power of science and engineering in doing astonishing and important things. We respect science as the author of penicillin, television, automobiles, and the atom bomb. But, once established, the authority of science is no different from the authority of the church or the authority of the state. Authority can be asserted both in controlling people's actions and in sanctioning them. To those whom Christianity fails to make good, it does not fail to give Christian marriage, Christian burial, and Christian holidays. *Christian* has served as a term of approbation for good men and deeds, but it has sometimes been used as a sanction for pretty bad ones. So has it been with *patriotic* and is now with *scientific*.

Thus in the age of the authority of science, people believe that a new pill will cure colds, "scientifically" of course, because they want to believe that their colds can be cured by a new remedy, but they may refuse to believe that fluorinated water is good for children's teeth, either because they distrust government or because they hate trouble and taxes. Whether these beliefs are true or not has nothing to do with the case. In the social use of science as authority, truth and falsity are irrelevant. The authority is recognized and it is invoked, but the occasion has little to do with the particular nature of the authority.

In the tremendous popularity of science, its social uses have naturally extended beyond those of grist for the philosophical mill and authority for an increasing proportion of beliefs, preferences, and modes of conduct. In today's world, science has also become the basis of that persistent social element, the magical.

One can quickly identify a minor manifestation of this fact in fantasy and in a great deal of science fiction. How many times have you mused on living forever? In an earlier day one achieved eternal carnal existence through Satan or magic; now one reads about its being achieved through science. Invincibility is to be had by the use of force fields. Have you deplored the exertion of walking? In the future, you will "scientifically" whisk yourself here and there by use of *psi* phenomena, a new code word for the power of mind.

Here we easily detect a magical element which is also found in many social uses of science lying outside written fantasy. We sense it in the magical ease with which things are done, in the complete absence of slow, painstaking labor, the stupendous effort involved in adding one little thing which is both new and true to our picture of the universe, or in applying such knowledge as we have to some technological end.

An outstanding characteristic of science as science is revealed in the years on years of hard, hard work of many people in the same field. Hubbard with dianetics, Velikovsky with his theories of astronomy and history, and others like them, are quite different. Theirs are individual products which, however much work by one man they may represent, show little investment of effort comparable with the tremendous scope of the fields they pretend to cover. Thus, the magical element can be recognized by the ease with which things are done, either in fiction or in pretended fact. We can also recognize the magical element through content.

One property of magic is that all words and combinations of words means something. The dying Napoleon felt that he needed *stronger* medicines. I am sure that here nothing like purity or dilution was meant, nor do I believe that even violence of effect on the human system was indicated; emetics and poisons can be strong in this sense. Almost certainly what he meant was a magical strength, a strength in combating illness. A more specific example of medical magic is the obsolete *theriac*, the universal antidote. At one time, few doubted that theriac signified something; the only question was, how to make theriac.

The magician works with words; he has a fixed idea that he knows or can find out what they mean, and he seeks to bind them to his ends with spells. Throughout the ages we have heard of the alkahest, the philosopher's stone, the secret of life, the secret of flight, the secret of the atom bomb, things with which man should not tamper. I believe that there is a strong magical element in some seemingly more reasonable phrases, such as a cure for old age, a cure for cancer, a cure for the common cold. Magic believes in all words, without question, and it seeks the corresponding spells.

A spell is often called *the secret* of something. The secret of something is very unlike scientific or engineering knowledge or skill. The magical secret can be imparted to anyone, regardless of intelligence or skill. Once in possession of the secret of life, a person can create life, or alternatively, he can live forever, whatever his training or skill. Presumably, anyone knowing the secret of flight could fly, but when phrases become embarrassingly silly they are conveniently forgotten by the believers in magic.

One may expect seekers after eternal life, physical or ghostly, in any age, and not worry much about it. However, *magical secrets* are overwhelmingly popular in these days, and they get all mixed up with real, everyday secrets in a way that hinders our work and endangers our security.

Sometimes, when I contemplate the widespread popularity of

secrets, I am exasperated into believing that the word has a sexual significance for its most persistent users. Memory of the labels attached to the various organs of the nude male figure in the old patent medicine almanacs tend to confirm this. Does the exaggerated concern and emotional disturbance of public figures who express fear that we may lose our secrets give a ready clue to what they really fear losing?

We cannot avoid talk about secrets and secrecy, and most of this talk is associated with science, at least in the sense that magic is one of the social uses of science. If security is taken seriously, we should learn to distinguish real secrets from secrets whose content is magical.

What, for instance, was our chief secret of microwave radar in the last war? The secret was that we had the apparatus in an effective form and the Germans didn't know this. We used it against submarines, and for a long time the Germans didn't know how their submarines were being located.

Although the work on microwave radar gave us many valuable component parts, such as the cavity magnetron which the Germans didn't have, I am convinced that they could have made good microwave radars if only they had known that the radars were worth making. If they had learned how much we were spending in this field, they probably would have entered the field. The truly invaluable secret that we were working hard in this field and spending a lot of money was well kept, to the great hurt of the Germans. I cannot be as sure in the case of the atom bomb, but I do know that the Germans had no idea we were spending large sums in this field. Had they known, they might perhaps have put forth the effort needed to make atom bombs.

In the case of the proximity fuse, the secret was perhaps of a more technical nature; namely, that electronic devices can survive being fired from a gun. But this secret was a conjecture in the early stages of the work, rather than a technological fact, and so the real secret was that we had confidence that a proximity fuse could be made.

These very real and vitally important secrets are like the secret of the Trojan horse, which lay in the fact that it concealed men, and not in its detailed structure, or like Gideon's secret, that each of his soldiers had a lamp, rather than merely the captains of his companies. But many nonscientists want to believe in magical secrets, modern equivalents of the mistletoe which would slay Balder, the unprotected heel of Achilles, the strength-giving hair of Samson. The believer in magic feels powerless without a secret spell to slay his enemy, a secret formula, a secret component, a secret wonder-working ingredient. He pays little heed to and may actually be care-less about really important secrets concerning judgment, intent, and magnitude of effort. And he firmly believes, not only that magical secrets of science exist somewhere in all those classified documents, but that this huge, rich, hard-working country can easily be put in jeopardy if these magical secrets are given into less capable hands.

After considering examples familiar to all of us, it is tempting to turn to that land of wonderful nonsense, the Soviet Union, in which the social uses of science are a part of state dogma, so that economics, politics, the arts, and even science itself must be "scientific" in a sense that we usually associate with patent medicine advertisements and intellectual fringes. Here, however, I feel on unsure ground. Is speculation about such a distant land perhaps the same sort of ama-teur philosophizing for which I have chided scientists?

Indeed, persuasive as it may be to physical scientists, what I have said about our own social uses of science, as grist for the philosophi-cal mill, as the universal authority, and as the treasurehouse of magic and the repository of spells, will perhaps seem to others insufficiently documented. How can this be remedied? I sincerely hope that someone, possibly an energetic young doctoral candidate, may apply the methods of classical social science to this problem, and undertake that painful process of research, often so foreign to the physical sciences, which consists of reading books, journals, and documents, of talking purposefully to people, and of making card indices, so that he may finally arrive at and defend an authoritative thesis on the social uses of science.

Freedom in Research*

Like food, we should have it in sufficient measure, but we should not need to assure ourselves by gluttony

IN these days, freedom is mentioned so often in connection with research that a naïve person might come to believe that freedom is, if not an end in itself, at least a sovereign ingredient which ensures success.

Whatever freedom may be, we sometimes feel that we want it above all things; we long for freedom, not only from the tyranny of people and events but from the weaknesses of flesh and spirit, from our appetites and our aspirations alike. This freedom, which I believe we shall eventually have in full measure, is very different from freedom as it appears to a willful child—having his own way from moment to moment, regardless of consequences to himself or others.

If there are indeed many sorts of freedom, then many sorts of freedom may be important in research. However, we will merely become confused by trying to identify freedom with the course and aim of research. The course of research is intelligent, creative, and enthuiastic work toward an end. The aim of research is new understanding or new accomplishment. Freedom will be important to research insofar as it contributes to the wise choice of problems and to the enthusiastic and successful pursuit of solutions.

It seems clear that the research worker must be free to work on a problem which challenges and interests him and which is yet within his capabilities, rather than a problem which he finds dull or which is beyond his abilities. He must be free to equip himself adequately to tackle his problem, with physical apparatus, of course, and also intellectually, through study or through contact with others, near or

* Reprinted by permission of John R. Pierce from *Science,* Vol. 130 (September 4, 1959) , 540–542.

far. Without a good measure of such freedom, successful research just can't be carried out.

However, freedom should be like the food we eat. We should have a sufficient measure of freedom at hand when we need it. It should not be necessary for us to reassure ourselves about our freedom by engaging in ostentatious discussions or acts of freedom any more than it is for us to assure ourselves of continued sustenance by ostentatious gluttony. Indeed, a mania for freedom may be just as destructive to research as a lack of it.

We all know people who come around with a wonderful new idea every month, week, or day (maybe it just seems like once a day). I don't believe that even a great genius has that many ideas worthy of his serious effort. The man with an idea a day is unlikely to do anything substantial about any idea. He may become disgruntled because he cannot force others to work on his ideas, or he may unhappily work on one idea and bemoan the tyranny of the world in general. In no case is he apt either to make himself happy or to enrich the world.

Freedom does not even require that a man work on his own ideas. To do so is fine if the ideas are the best ones at hand. But, above all, a man needs to work on good, well-chosen ideas. Eminent and creative mathematicians have worked on Hilbert's problems of their own free will ever since Hilbert propounded them. First-rate scientists have traveled halfway around the world to work under a particular person or with a particular group and have worked gladly on problems suggested by the person or pursued by the group. Many a first-rate man has thanked his lucky stars that someone suggested that he do this or that. The idea may come from a colleague near or far, or from a "boss" who is older, wiser, or cleverer than the man himself.

Still, one does need freedom in choosing problems. It is deadly when a man feels that a problem is forced upon him, and even more deadly when he feels that it is a bad problem, either because the problem is just no good or because the problem is beneath or beyond his capabilities.

A man certainly doesn't need to exercise his freedom every day just to prove that it is still there, but it is a terrible thing to lose freedom, especially if it is lost little by little, so that he does not miss it until it is too late, or, even worse, does not realize that it is gone.

What, then, are the enemies of freedom? What can make a

research worker unfree? I believe that several rather different things can do this.

DEMANDS OF RESPONSIBILITY

It seems to me that freedom is an empty word unless it implies *real* alternatives among which there is some uncertainty about what one's choice will be. If this is so, responsibility is certainly one of the greatest enemies of freedom. The trouble is, however, that responsibility has its good features, too, so that everyone must arrive at some compromise between responsibility and freedom.

Most of us would find it easier to spend six months here and a year there or to change jobs entirely if it weren't for our wives and children. Some men solve this problem by not marrying. Some leave their wives and children to shift for themselves, and thereby gain in freedom.

Brain children, too, fetter some of us. The idea-a-day man is apt to be irresponsible concerning his ideas. He hopes, of course, that someone else will nurture them from bare existence into viability in a world of ruthless competition. Indeed, the chronic begetter of ideas may become angry when no one else gives his offspring the attention he is unwilling to lavish on them.

More responsible researchers pick a promising idea and spend endless time and effort helping it to find its place in the world. Some, indeed, unwisely go so far as to want to monopolize the idea after it has become self-supporting and has found its way into the lives of others.

Whenever we assume responsibility for an idea or a project, whenever we espouse it as our own, whenever we hold ourselves responsible for its fate, we have lost a part of our freedom. However, such a loss is necessary if we are to accomplish anything.

Some people get themselves saddled with other sorts of responsibility. They have to decide or help decide who should be hired, who should be fired, how big a raise a man should get. They have to worry and fight about budgets, space, and rules and regulations. All this isn't so bad, but what really takes their time is the work of others.

I may be wrong, but I think that, by and large, research workers, even good ones, suffer more frequently from lack of help than from lack of freedom. It isn't merely that they need help in coping with nontechnical problems. They need help in choosing problems wisely, help in overcoming difficulties in their work, help in judging whether what they are doing is good or bad, help in getting rid of old projects which are really done, and help in getting into new things which will be important and attractive. They also need not only encouragement for themselves but help in seeing that their work receives the recognition which it deserves. Only very rarely is a man completely self-sufficient. I know that I have benefited from and appreciated tremendously the ideas and help I have got from others.

Responsibility, both responsibility with respect to our own lives and ideas and responsibility with respect to the ideas and lives of others, is sure to cost us a great deal of our freedom. However, we just can't get on without responsibility, and we must put up with the loss. We should, however, particularly realize that the more responsibility we assume for ourselves, the less anyone else has to, or will, assume for us.

Another thing that we can't do without is apparatus. Some ideas, some projects, call for lots of expensive equipment. If a man has acquired a large-scale accelerator, a big radio telescope, or a large-scale computer, or if he has set to work on a large-scale experimental system of some sort, he is not likely to walk out on it because an attractive idea in some other field occurs to him. If a systems experiment is shackling him, he can abandon it if it is bad or complete it if it is good, but if he has an accelerator, a radio telescope, or a computer around his neck, he may be stuck in a field for life. This isn't fatal, of course; he can direct his thoughts to the field in question and have and pursue ideas in that field only. But he has lost freedom in that there is little chance that he will actually do something else, however much he may daydream about it. If he wants to recover his freedom, he can perhaps find a substitute, put him in charge, and leave him holding the bag.

SPECIALIZATION HAS ITS DRAWBACKS

Another way we can lose freedom is through excessive and unwise specialization, which can eventually leave us no alternatives to choose among. At any moment any man should be better able to cope with the problems he is currently working on than with others.

However, the problems in a field can be made to last forever, but the real need for and value of research in a narrow field may dry up and vanish. Or, a man may be a fine pioneer in a field but may not be suited to do the refined and mathematically difficult work which becomes necessary as time passes. Wisdom and good sense may dictate that he stop what he is doing and turn to something else. But he is scarcely free if he has lost the ability to do so.

A man can lose the freedom to change his work by allowing himself to become intellectually incompetent to deal effectively with anything outside his current narrow field of specialization, or he can lose this freedom of choice by becoming so emotionally involved in his field that he cannot bear to leave it. He can also lose any real freedom of choice by convincing himself that he has some commercial and social stake in a field, a stake he cannot afford to lose; he can convince himself that he is valuable only because of his expert knowledge, or is looked up to only because of it.

Still, just as we must have responsibility and apparatus, so too we must have some degree of specialization, even if this does cut into our freedom. There is one curtailer of freedom, however, with which I think we could well dispense. That is snobbishness.

A college president once described to me a sort of pecking order of the sciences. According to him, the mathematicians look down on the physicists, the physicists on the chemists, the chemists on the biologists, and the biologists on the psychologists.

One sure and utterly frivolous and destructive way for a man to lose his freedom is for him to feel overwhelmingly impelled to choose his work, not on the basis of its suitability to his talents, not on the basis of its interest to him, not on the basis of its urgency or importance, but rather on the basis of its status in the eyes of some person, group, society, journal, or whatnot.

Finally, what might be called management (though it includes institutional policies of long standing as well as people) can affect the researcher's freedom.

ON CHANGING JOBS

Sometimes a research worker may not have adequate funds for travel or for telephone calls, or he may find it difficult to get adequate apparatus or to get it promptly. These matters are frequently mentioned in connection with government laboratories. It is clear, however, that in these days of competition for engineers and scientists, a good man doesn't have to put up with such handicaps. He can go elsewhere to escape them, and he will.

Sometimes a man may feel that the scope of research in the institution where he works does not coincide with or include his interests. While an exceptional man may drastically alter the place at which he works (and this is desirable from time to time), a good man generally goes to a particular place because he is interested in the field and impressed by the quality of work done there.

A lone man, even a very competent one, is bound to have much more freedom in changing his job than he has in changing what his associates are doing. This doesn't mean that he shouldn't try the latter, but a broad change in the nature or direction of the work of an institution involves other people's freedom as well as his own.

Finally, there can be a very real personal threat to a man's freedom: the tyranny of a boss. For research, it is absolutely essential that a man work on problems that he believes to be good problems for him and that he tackle them in a way in which he has confidence. We have noted that a man doesn't necessarily have to invent the problem or the general approach toward its solution himself.

Further, it is essential that if he does have a good idea, he should feel free to explore it (we have seen that he will not necessarily do so). He must further be convinced that his colleagues, including colleagues who may be bosses, welcome new ideas and are anxious to see them pursued and exploited. A free—indeed, a cutthroat—competition among ideas is essential to research. It seems to me that a researcher should have no freedom to make other able people work on his ideas rather than on their own, beyond what he can make them want to do through persuasion based on the merits of his ideas.

Fortunately, today good people don't have to work under any other conditions. There is tremendous competition for good workers with good ideas. A man who really suffers from the tyranny of the boss can go to some other department or to some other company. And if a boss is so tyrannous that good men leave him, he won't last forever.

Still, men do complain about the tyranny of jobs and bosses. It is my observation that these are seldom the best men. In fact, often they are men who have amply demonstrated their inability to do research when left completely to themselves, and sometimes they are men who should not try to do research under any circumstances.

Clearly, freedom is vitally important to research, but other somewhat inconsistent things are important, too. Responsibilities of one sort or another keep us from following up every idea or inclination we have. Apparatus ties us down. Concentration on one subject lessens our ability to tackle another. Then too, we may lose our freedom foolishly. Snobbishness may dictate our course of action. Or we may work in a poor environment, inadequately provided for, or with a tyrannous boss to browbeat us. But, in this day and age we are foolish if we put up with such things, unless we really aren't good enough to find another environment—or unless conditions aren't as bad as we think they are after all.

Discovery, Invention, and Society*

AT one time, man's environment consisted of natural objects—grains and vegetables, cows and horses, rivers, lakes, and seas—together with plows and boats, houses and mills, things man-made, but produced more through traditional skill than through deep intellectual understanding. Today we use trains and automobiles rather than barges and horses, and we live among a host of things which had no counterpart in an earlier time, and which would have found no place in an earlier society. These new things include airplanes and electric power, but telephones, television, and computers are even better examples.

All these things have profoundly altered our lives, but in one way they have not altered the way in which we live them. Today's child accepts the telephone and television with the same sense of familiarity and lack of understanding that earlier generations accorded natural phenomena. We do not need to know the physical basis of telephony in order to use a telephone anymore than we need to understand the biological intricacies of a horse in order to ride one. Familiarity and use are the same in each case. But the telephone is a product of man, and the telephone system, a huge and intricate assembly of complicated parts, is the outgrowth of research and understanding as we know them in science.

This sort of understanding is powerful in our world, but it is rare in connection with any common thing that is not a product of science and technology. For example, we talk and read and write every day, but we understand very little about language. In the past decade, attempts to use the computer to translate from one language to another have forcibly emphasized how little we do understand this universal intellectual tool.

* From a talk given at California Institute of Technology on October 15, 1966.

Men have studied languages for centuries. In attempts at machine translation, it soon became apparent that an accurate grammar would be necessary, a grammar by means of which a computer could parse a sentence unambiguously (as we almost always can) and a grammar by means of which all grammatical and no ungrammatical utterances could be constructed. It became equally apparent that the accumulated wisdom of linguists could not supply even a reasonably satisfactory grammar for any language. The grammars they gave us are like tips for playing good golf. With their aid—and with the aid of our hidden and unformulated skills of speech—we can construct grammatical (and meaningful) sentences, and we can interpret and parse such sentences. But we don't consciously understand how we do this, and so we cannot tell a computer how to do it. Language is central to our life and thought. Yet, in the sense that we use *understanding* in science, we do not understand language.

There is an increasing side to our life which is quite different. Everyone uses language, but no one understands how we use it. In contrast, everyone uses television sets and telephones, and a few people do understand them deeply. Partly, this is because a radio or a telephone is very much simpler than a language or a human being. Chiefly, however, we understand a radio or telephone because it has been created according to our understanding. Through our understanding of science, we see how we can make a useful device. We do this in a way that is understandable to us. It is no wonder, then, that the operation of the final product is understandable.

Science and technology inject into our environment an increasing part that is inherently understandable and controllable. To this we adapt, behaviorally, linguistically, and in attitude, in the old mysterious way in which man has always managed to live. In so doing we acquire new needs and new standards. A society which functioned well in the absence of telephones, automobiles, and electronic power is replaced by a society which would collapse without these present necessities.

Communication is a particularly apt field in which to discuss and illustrate the impact, actual and potential, of the understanding of science and the power of technology on society. Electrical communication has changed our lives profoundly within the span of our memories.

Further, electrical communication clearly exemplifies the applicability and power of science. Few industries have a deeper or broader technological base. Within my lifetime, communication has been profoundly changed by advances in electron tubes, by a rapidly changing solid-state art which has displaced these, by the invention and control of polymers which have replaced wood, paper, rubber, and even metals, and by a mathematical and logical insight into ways of organizing digital systems, such as computers and telephone switching systems.

Finally, electrical communication illustrates, as no other field can, the range from the comparatively simple, exemplified by the local broadcasting station and the home receiver, to the incredibly complicated and interdependent, exemplified in common-carrier communication systems.

This division between the technologically simple and the technologically complex reflects a difference in the purpose and function of mass communication, such as television, and the purpose and function of personal communication, such as telephony. Mass communication is necessarily aimed at majorities or large minorities. It is one way; it is aimed from the few to the many. It is a unifying and conservative element in our society. As such, its effects have been tremendous.

We are rapidly approaching a society without sticks or boondocks, except those which are growing in the central slums of metropolitan areas. Television brings into the remotest home launchings from Cape Kennedy, sports from all parts of the continent, even (via satellite) live events from across the ocean, and a nationally uniform brand of music, comedy, and soap opera.

Some crusty people decry television for being what it is rather than what it isn't. They have an easy remedy at hand; if they have a television set, they can turn it off. This is certainly cheaper than trying to turn television into what it can't be—books, or the theater, or the schools. Most of us enjoy TV in varying degrees, and find that it has become a necessary part of our lives. The center of our society is no longer a physical region, it is a medium of communication which pours forth in every home.

In the face of television, it is difficult for differences of dialect, of interest, or of attitude to persist. This makes television the greatest unifying force ever to act upon man. A voice and a picture on television may not yet be able to tell us what to think about a matter, but they very effectively decide what we will be thinking about, and that may be as remote physically as the war in Viet Nam. Here, on the other side of the globe, we are made conscious of political implications which escape most of the Vietnamese themselves, who know government only through death and taxes.

Television is a direct and powerful tool in the hands of central government. The President and members of his administration can appeal directly to the people, without distortion or deletion of what they want to say. And what they say directly to the people, the newspapers must handle somehow.

This is powerful in a society which is already unified, but its impact and power could be far greater in an emerging nation which for its well-being and indeed its survival must achieve some sort of national unity and effective government.

The impact of the telephone and other common-carrier communications is quite different from that of mass communication. The telephone is inherently the tool of the individual, not of the majority or the society. It is the means by which we conduct the business of life—ordering groceries, calling the doctor, making appointments and reservations. It is our social tool in keeping in touch with friends and relatives, arranging dates, dinners, parties, and trips. And it is our intellectual tool in calling informed acquaintances to find out what is really behind public statements, and even in arranging protest marches and demonstrations.

Unlike mass communications, which could have a profound impact on even a primitive society, the telephone is inherently a part of a way of life which has been shaped by automobiles, and airplanes, and electric power, and standardized, uniform merchandise, and a pattern of credit, and, especially, by the telephone itself. We use the telephone because we have come to have interests that lie beyond the home, the family, and the neighborhood. We use the telephone because we can and are willing to buy without shopping, on the basis of past experience and information provided by ads which reach us by mail or through newspapers. It seems to me that except for some government and business usage, a telephone system would have little immediate impact or value in a primitive society. Its widespread use is a reflection of our way of life, a way of life which the telephone itself has helped to bring into being.

So far, I have cited communication as an example of the impact

of science and technology—of intellectual understanding, if you will
—on society; and I have indicated how important this can be in
the utterly different fields of mass communication, as exemplified by
television, and of individual communication, as exemplified by telephony. I have not, however, indicated how the revolutionary powers
of communication came into being. Their source is discovery and
invention. While this is, I hope, a plausible and simple statement,
it is an important one. Today we hear much about meeting the
needs of society, and about planning and systems analysis and systems engineering as means for meeting those needs.

Planning and systems analysis and systems engineering are vital
parts of technology. They are essential in making good and effective
use of what we have at hand. They may even be effective in pointing
out lacks which stand in the way of accomplishing what we want to
do. Discovery and invention may—or may not—then remedy such
recognized deficiencies. But discovery and invention often take us off
on some entirely different tack.

I am sure that when Alexander Graham Bell invented the telephone, what common-carrier communication felt it *really* needed
was better multiplex telegraphy, and perhaps practical automatic
telegraphy. In fact, Bell was working on a new kind of multiplex
telegraph—the harmonic telegraph—when he invented the telephone. What the world got through this invention was a revolutionary system of communication that has swamped the telegram and,
indeed, the letter as means of interpersonal communication.

We do what we can, not what we think we should or what we
want to do. And needs are as often created as satisfied by discovery
and invention.

Lee De Forest was seeking a detector for wireless telegraphy when
he invented the vacuum tube. The invention led to worldwide telephony and to radio broadcasting.

Television languished as an interesting idea for years until science
and technology gave us an advanced electronic art and Vladimir K.
Zworykin invented the iconoscope.

Charles Babbage tried to make a very well-thought-out and sophis-
ticated computer in the nineteenth century and failed. Around 1940,
the computer was reinvented and easily realized by Howard H.
Aiken and George Stibitz, using the art supplied by telephone
switching. The vacuum tube made it possible for J. Presper Eckert

and John W. Mauchly to make a fast electronic calculator. John Von Neumann provided the stored program. And the transistor made the computer economical, reliable, and profitable.

Discovery and invention have been the crucial elements in inaugurating and changing the course of communication. Systems engineering and systems development have been necessary in effectively exploiting discovery and invention, in realizing their full impact. But in most cases the discoverers and inventors have convincingly demonstrated the power and potentialities of what they have done before it seriously engaged the attention of systems engineers.

In the field of communication and in other fields, discovery and invention will continue to provide a potential for changing the world we live in, and, through systems planning and systems engineering, changes will be realized. What these changes will do to our life I can only guess. They will certainly provide an environment as different from that of today as today's world is different from the pre-telephone, pre-automobile, pre-airplane world. A hope of mine is that in the future we will be able to live where we like, travel chiefly for pleasure, and communicate to work. Perhaps this is too optimistic.

The certainty is that science provides an understanding which is alien to everyday life. We understand little in this way, but what little understanding we have is extremely powerful. Through research and development, this understanding has so altered our environment that we live lives which are essentially different from those of earlier generations. And science and technology are now creating, through advances in communications as well as in many other fields, an entirely new environment in which life will again be different. As always, man will adapt to this world by apprenticeship, by the same sort of learning without understanding that enables us all to speak and to walk. The man who successfully lives in the world of the future need not understand that world in the sense of scientific understanding, but it is the understanding of science which is bringing that world into being.

Planning and Readiness*

TODAY, no wise man would undertake to operate a government, a business, or his life without appropriate planning. Forecasting and planning have become a necessary as well as a valuable part of our world.

Nonetheless, history makes it plain that planning must have inherent fallibilities. The world of today and its problems are products of discovery and invention. Our life is different from life a century ago because of a vigorous and successful pursuit of radical and probably unforeseeable advances in scientific agriculture, which freed a large fraction of the population from the farms, and an equally eager exploitation of inventions or innovations such as the automobile, the airplane, electric power, telephony, and television, which have made possible a highly unified life in which individuals and enterprises can be widely dispersed. The urbanization of our population is very real, but our urban areas and the distribution functions among them are very different from those of a century ago. How could men of a century ago have planned for the world of today? It took more than planning to get us where we are.

Thus, changes in our life hinge only in part on the importance and fallibilities of planning. I want to emphasize even more the importance of technological readiness. By this I mean a capability of management and an availability of facilities for research, development, and manufacture which make it possible, not only to introduce new and desirable things into our society, but also to respond quickly and effectively to the introduction of new things, so that rapid innovation and growth can be fostered at a price society and industry can afford.

* Reprinted with permission from "Forecasting the Future," *Science Journal,* Vol. 3, No. 10 (October, 1967), 76–81.

It would certainly be possible to have a completely planned society, either by ruling out innovation, or by adapting it to the pace of rational planning. Our own society, with its many fallibilities, is more the result of readiness for discovery and innovation than it is the result of planning. Despite our society's many faults, there seems little reason to believe that it is inferior to what we would get if planning rather than discovery and innovation shaped the future.

In general, orderly growth in the past seems to commend planning. It almost leads us to believe that we can plan by extrapolation. When we plot population, number of telephones, etc. on semilog paper, we most commonly get almost straight lines. Figure 1 is an example. This shows a nearly exponential rise in gross national product, in population, and in the number of telephones in the United States. Such a plot convinces us that it would be madness not to provide the technological resources and the capital necessary to expand conventional telephone service at the indicated rate. The

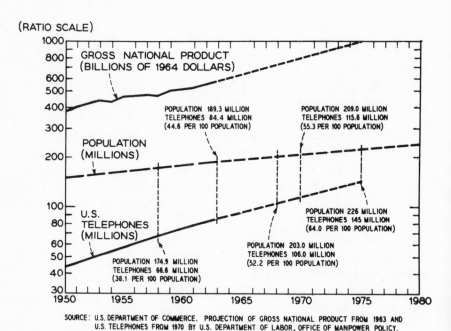

SOURCE: U.S. DEPARTMENT OF COMMERCE. PROJECTION OF GROSS NATIONAL PRODUCT FROM 1963 AND U.S. TELEPHONES FROM 1970 BY U.S. DEPARTMENT OF LABOR, OFFICE OF MANPOWER POLICY, EVALUATION, AND RESEARCH.

FIG. 1

consequence of the failure of either adequate capital or adequate technological resources would be unfilled orders for telephone service, which would inevitably result in a diminution in the rate of growth as people had to rely in some degree on other methods of communication.

If we examine growth over a somewhat longer period and in more detail, we see that there are perturbations from exponential growth. Figure 2 shows the total number of telephones in the United States for the period from 1921 to 1966. There is a decided dip following 1931, which we may attribute to the depression. There is also a

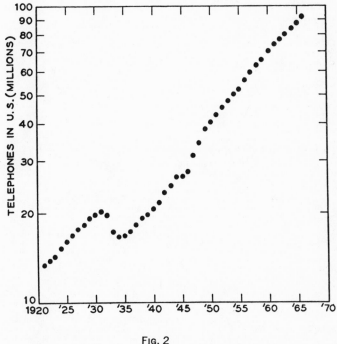

Fig. 2

smaller wiggle around 1945, which must be associated with World War II. So, planners have to take into account, as best they can, economic conditions and major political upheavals.

In part, the smooth overall growth in the number of telephones is

a reflection of many factors and many uses. For instance, as we can
see from Figure 3, the number of overseas telephone messages has
been increasing recently at the rate of about 17 percent per year.
The lower points of Figure 4 indicate that domestic long-
distance messages have been increasing recently at the rate of about
14 percent per year. But the lower points are not the total long-
distance traffic, which is represented by the upper points. The dis-
continuity at 1962 accompanied the introduction of WATS and
DTWX—that is, wide area telephone service at a flat rate, and dialed
teletypewriter service over phone lines. These service offerings
appear to have added an increment to the volume of conventional
usage but do not seem likely to have made an appreciable change in
rate of growth.

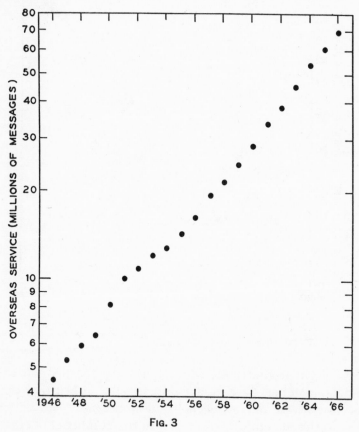

FIG. 3

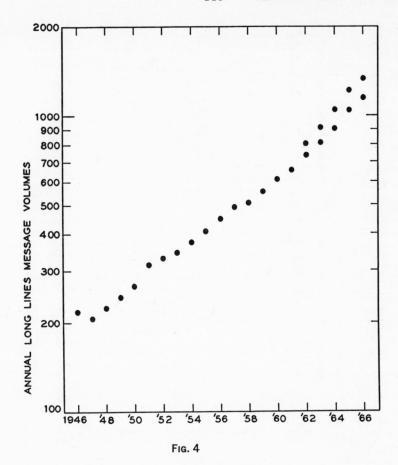

FIG. 4

WATS and DTWX produced only a small increase in the total volume of service, probably because they extended the use of an already existing type of communication. We see more profound effects in the expansion of a new service, such as television. Figure 5 shows, for the United States, growth in TV sets in use, in homes with TV sets, and in annual production of TV sets. It would be misleading to regard the growths of the first two as exponential, and the annual production of TV sets shows ups and downs following an initial period of extremely rapid growth.

This growth of TV is reflected in the growth of channels which common carriers supply. Figure 6 shows the miles of available

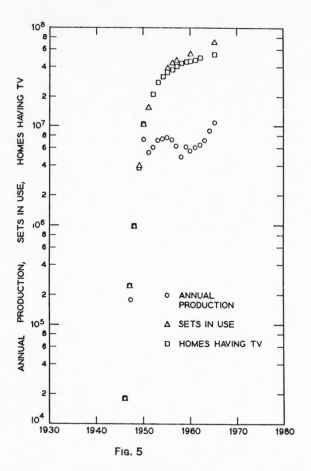

FIG. 5

video-grade channels in the United States. We see a growth from almost none in 1947 to something near a saturation in 1954, followed by a return to a 10-15- percent annual increase. The initial period of growth corresponds to the growth of broadcast television. What are we to think of the small growth beyond 1954?

In one sense, this growth is illusory, for it is made up mainly of channels used for short periods of time only. It corresponds not so much to a growth in broadcast television as to the use of circuits for short times in covering special events.

Should we then believe that the growth will be small following 1966? On the contrary, we may be due for another spurt of growth.

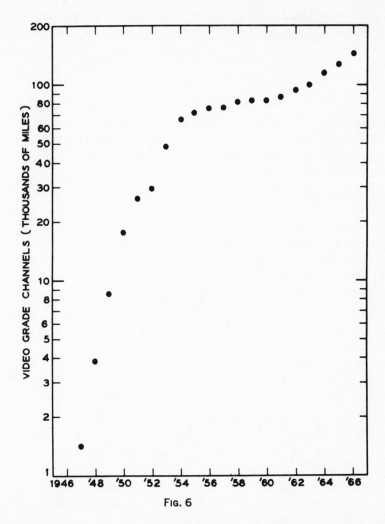

FIG. 6

Several things could give rise to this. One is the increased use of television for industrial purposes and for educational purposes in col-
leges and schools. Another is the possibility of an expansion of
broadcast television through public service programs financed in
new ways. A third is supplying programs for the ultrahigh-frequency
television channels which are opening up. A fourth possibility of
growth is opened up by the expansion of community antenna television which permits in a large number of areas the distribution of

more channels that does broadcast television, in which assignment of radio frequency channels without interference limits the number of channels available in many places.

The steady telephone growth shown in Figure 4 is relevant to readiness as well as to planning. The first coaxial cable system, the first part of the American common-carrier network with a broad enough band for television, was put into commercial service in 1941. The development of this system was amply justified by telephone needs, but I am sure that wise men in management realized that it would have an application in television. Indeed, it not only had an application; it made interconnection of television stations possible during the period up to 1950, when broadband microwave systems were first introduced into the common-carrier network.

Again, the development of the TD-2 microwave system was justified for telephone traffic. Today, about 60 percent of toll circuits are provided by microwave systems. Nonetheless, it was foreseen that this system would be a means for meeting television interconnection and networking needs. It was a particularly apt means because the first cost of a microwave system is less than that of a cable system, and the installation is less complicated.

While wisdom enabled people to foresee that a coaxial cable system and a microwave radio relay system would be useful and, indeed, essential in the development of television, I do not think that all the wisdom or planning in the world would have enabled anyone to tell just where the number of video-grade circuits would level off or what the growth rate would be thereafter. What was needed for the successful growth of television interconnection and networking were adequate technological resources to meet a demand that was foreseen, adequate capital to meet the demand as it came, and sufficiently fast technological response in manufacture and installation.

If we look still further behind the scenes, we see all sorts of surprisingly rapid changes are embedded in the exponential growth of the overall common-carrier communication plant. For instance, Figure 7 shows the annual production of a particular carrier system which is an exceedingly useful part of the telephone plant, a system which, once produced and installed, will continue to give good service for many years. But by 1965 the manufacture of something

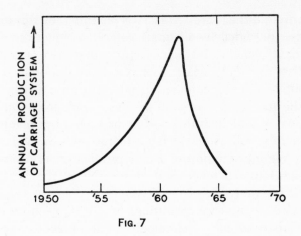

FIG. 7

which was a valuable novelty in 1950 was well on its way to extinction.

Such rapid technological change has more than short-term effects within the common-carrier plant; it has long-term effects on the growth of telephony. Growing traffic called for more telephone service. The newer and newer means which were used to provide more telephone circuits: cable, carrier-on-cable, coaxial cable of rapidly increasing capacity, and microwave radio of rapidly increasing capacity, made telephone circuits cheaper. This in turn increased the demand for long-distance service and allowed further reduction in cost through economies of scale. And the progress which was responsible for expansion of telephone service also gave us broadband transmission systems which have made possible video transmission and the rapid transmission of data.

Thus, even when rates of exponential growth for established services are sluggish compared with the rate at which technological innovation changes the internal appearance of the common-carrier plant, their existence, and the plant expansion they require, can have profound social implications for our society. We live in a man-made world, in which our environment is increasingly the product of science and technology. Inasmuch as one area of science or technology serves man well, conveniently, and economically, that area of service will expand, as we have seen expansion in air travel, automobiles, television, and telephony. Inasmuch as as area of technology fails to serve man well, either through lack of planning, or through lack of the readiness provided by adequate capital, adequate research, and adequate development and manufacture, that area of our life will fall into disrepute and disease. Society will take another course.

I am confident that technology is taking us into a surprising new world of the future. But beyond discovery and invention, how can we attain that world? Planning will be necessary, but planning is not easy. It is hard to tell when the fantastic rate of growth characteristic of the effective introduction of a new product or service will begin, and it is hard to tell when and at what level the initial rate of growth will level off.

Even more than wise planning, we will need readiness of resources—financial and technological—in order to provide new forms of communication and to respond flexibly to people's demand for them. We must plan as hard and wisely as we can, but we must be ready for the inevitable unplanned deviations and unexpected opportunities.

IV
But Is It Art?

For some years the public has been exposed to strange varieties of art, including aleatory art and computer art.

Stochastic *means something that includes randomness or change.* Ergodic *is narrower than stochastic; the odds don't change with time.* Random *means unpredictable.*

Both the unpredictable behavior of dice and more predictable behavior of computers find their place in the material of this section. What about aleatory? *Aleatory is an old English word which has a particular meaning in law, but mathematicians translate the French* aléatoire *as stochastic, not aleatory. This is a minor illustration of the gulf between the two cultures.*

Chance Remarks*

THERE has been a lot in the papers recently about cybernetics and the theory of communications but, as usual, *Astounding Science Fiction* was ahead of all others—back at least as far as 1943 and Raymond F. Jones's story, "Fifty Million Monkeys." You may remember the "semantic analyzer" which selected meaningful words from random letters. Now something very like that has appeared in the most respectable sort of print.

It was a long and indirect route which led from Jones's story to an authoritative publication, "A Mathematical Theory of Communication," by Dr. C. E. Shannon. Dr. Shannon, who is now at the Bell Telephone Laboratories, is a product of the Massachusetts Institute of Technology and of the Institute for Advanced Study at Princeton. His accomplishments include the application of Boolean Algebra—a symbolic logic—to the problem of telephone switching. His new work, which won him the Morris Liebman Memorial Prize of the Institute of Radio Engineers, is a fine exercise in multidimensional geometry and probability theory.

The whole field that Dr. Shannon covers is important, but it is so broad as to make a simple explanation exceedingly difficult. Too, much of the material, while of great technical importance, may seem to have little interest for anyone but an expert. But Part I, Section 2 of the paper, "The Discrete Source of Information," deals with something which seems right up the science fiction alley, that is, the statistical structure of written English.

It is immediately clear that English text is in some way set aside from mere combinations of letters. Subjectively, one easily tells whether text is English or whether it is not. There is, however, an objective distinction.

Dr. Shannon describes this by saying that written English is redundant. That is, more symbols are used than are needed to convey the information. Now, what is important is that the excess symbols are introduced according to certain rules, which a mathematician calls statistical laws or probabilities. For instance, q is always followed by u. Most of the rules are not this simple. However, a writer in mid-word or in mid-sentence does not — ordinarily — exercise complete freedom of choice in setting down the next letter or word. The choice of some letters or words is completely ruled out, or, in other words, such choices have zero probability. Among the letters or words allowed, some are more probable than others. For instance, because of our unconscious knowledge of such statistical rules, or of certain specific instances of them, we can correctly reconstruct most text—the reader can easily verify this— even if many of the individual letters have been erased or struck out. When we cannot, as in the case of some passages from Gertrude Stein or James Joyce, it is because there is something objectively un-English about the original text. That is, the text doesn't follow the rules. Granted conventional English text as a source from which to draw statistical rules, it is theoretically possible to tell English text from un-English sequences of symbols by applying statistical tests.

Dr. Shannon's work has led him to believe that English is about 50 percent redundant, that is, that one has about half as much freedom of choice as if symbols could be chosen with complete freedom. This is no trivial observation, for it has all sorts of implications. For instance, this degree of redundancy makes it just possible to construct crossword puzzles. If there were no redundancy, any arbitrary combination of letters would be a word. Thus, any set of letters could be read up or down as well as crosswise, and backward, too. There would be no puzzle to crosswords. If the redundancy were much greater than 50 percent, there would be so little freedom of choice in the sequence of letters that it would be impossible to achieve a crossword pattern. The degree of redundancy of English allows the construction of crossword patterns with some difficulty, and makes the language almost ideal for crossword puzzles. Conceivably, crossword puzzles could not succeed in some countries because the structure of the language would make them virtually impossible.

To the mathematician a language is a "stochastic—i.e., a statistical—process which generates a discrete sequence of symbols from a finite set." These symbols are the letters of the language, together with punctuation and spaces, if these occur. The stochastic process chooses these symbols in accordance with certain probabilities which involve the sequence of symbols already chosen. Thus, if part of a word or a sentence has been written down, the probability, as evaluated from ordinary English text, that the next letter will be *a* may be very high, while the probability that the next letter will be *e* may be very low, and these probabilities will depend on the preceding letters and the orders in which they occur—that is, on what has already been written down.

If the statistics of the language were completely known, it would be possible—again in theory—to evaluate exactly the saving which could be made in transmitting English text. It would also be possible to do other things of which we shall have a hint later. Of course, a knowledge of the whole statistical structure of a language is an unattainable ideal, but one need not for this reason forgo all knowledge. Indeed, Dr. Shannon has done a little preliminary exploration himself in a surprisingly simple and a rather interesting manner.

We already know from work on cryptography, and can obtain from other sources, a small part of the statistical laws of English text. Now, suppose we choose symbols—letters—by a chance process incorporating the rules which we know, and see how nearly the result resembles English. This will give us some clue as to the relative importance of the part of the statistical rules which we know and employ, and the unknown part of the statistics of the language.

Dr. Shannon gives first an exceedingly simple example:

XFMOL RXKHRJFFJUMZLPWCFWKCYJ FFJEYVKCQSGXYD
QPAAMKBZAACIBZLHJQD

Here the letters and spaces are successively drawn at random with equal probabilities for all symbols. Here, for instance, *r* and *z* are as common as *e* and *a*, which they certainly are not in English text. The combinations are un-English, unpronounceable and uninteresting. Mathematically, we say that the statistics are incorrect.

OCRO HLI NMIELWIS EU LL NBNESBYA TH EEI ALHENTTPA
OOBTTVA NAH BRL

Here letters were chosen, still independently, but with regard for their probabilities in English. If they were chosen from a hat, there would be more *e*'s in the hat than *z*'s, for instance. There is still, however, no rule connecting pairs of letters; there is no rule saying that *u* is the only letter which has any probability at all of following *q*. Still, some of the statistics of English have been taken into account, and the result is surprisingly more like English than the first sample. The letters do occasionally form wordlike combinations. Although it is not in the dictionary, OCRO is pronounceable. It is interesting to think of OCRO as a nonsense word, and to wonder who invented it. It was really begotten, although through a human agency, by an undistinguished copy of a book of random numbers. A machine following the rules could as easily have arrived at the combination.

ON IE ANTSOUTINYS ARE T INCTORE ST BE S DEAMY ACHIN D ILONASIVE TUCOOWE AT TEASONARE FUSO TIZIN ANDY TOBE SEACE CTISBE

This has some intriguing features. Here more of the statistics of English were observed, and each letter or space was chosen in accordance with its probability of following that preceding. If *q* had occurred in the example, it could have been followed only by *u*. This has resulted in combinations of symbols which strongly resemble English. ARE is a real word. INCTORE and ILONASIVE are not words, but they are very wordlike. DEAMY almost suggests meaning, and is perhaps worthy of remembrance. One begins to wonder if Dr. Shannon's work has some literary significance. Can senseless statistics perhaps add to our vocabulary?

IN NO IST LAT WHEY CRATICT FROURE BIRS GROCID PON-DENOME OF DEMONSTURES OF THE REPTAGIN IS REGO-ACTIONA OF CRE

To an unprejudiced reader, this is not only largely pronounceable, but it sounds like talk, and English talk more than anything else—it contains seven English words. Or, if you wish, the passage sounds like double-talk. It is perhaps difficult to believe that in constructing this passage no conscious effort was made to make up English-like combinations. The procedure of construction was, however, purely automatic; each letter was chosen in accordance with the probability of its following the ordered pair of letters preceding it.

It must be understood that, because of the increasingly elaborate statistics involved, these passages were increasingly difficult to construct. A complicated machine could do more, but without one it seemed impractical to go further, and to base a letter on a preceding ordered triplet of letters. We can, however, see where the process would lead. If we added letters according to rules involving three, four, five, and more preceding letters, we would gradually rule out as of zero probability all combinations which do not appear as words in the dictionary. We might as well, indeed, use words as our basis of choice, and Dr. Shannon has tried this, too. As a first example he chose words merely on the basis of their probability of appearing in English text:

REPRESENTING AND SPEEDILY IS AN GOOD APT OR COME CAN DIFFERENT NATURAL HERE HE THE A IN CAME THE TO OF TO EXPERT GRAY COME CAN DIFFERENT NATURAL TO FURNISHES THE LINE MESSAGE HAD BE THESE

This seems rather a retrogression. The statistics are unduly simple, for they provide no connection between words. With a great deal of effort, Dr. Shannon was able to provide such a connection, however. In obtaining the following passage, a pair of words was chosen at random in a novel. The novel was then read through until the second of these words was encountered again, and the word following it was inserted. Then that new word was sought out in a new context, and the word following it there was added, and so on. This laborious process evoked:

THE HEAD AND IN FRONTAL ATTACK ON AN ENGLISH WRITER THAT THE CHARACTER OF THIS POINT IS THERE-FORE ANOTHER METHOD FOR THE LETTERS THAT THE TIME OF WHO EVER TOLD THE PROBLEM FOR AN UNEX-PECTED

Here we have merely an example of words chosen randomly according to certain statistics. We may, however, have a strange feeling that we have seen something like this before. Certain passages in *Ulysses* and *Finnegans Wake* are scarcely more intelligible. Despite an apparent lack of connection, the passage has some subjective interest. I have a sympathetic concern for the predicament of the English writer. I would like to ask the author more about him. Unfortunately, there is no author to ask. I shall hear no more unless, perhaps, chance should answer my questions. One wonders if Dr. Shannon's work has philosophical implications.

Dr. Shannon stops at this point. The idea of pursuing the matter further is, however, tempting. By taking into account more and more statistics in the choice of letters, all letter combinations but English words could be ruled out. Can we, by the use of a more elaborate statistical choice of words, rule out all word combinations which don't make sense? At least we could construct something better organized than the last example.

Suppose, for instance, that a word were chosen in accordance with its probability of following the preceding three words. Although this might seem unduly difficult, a trick will overcome all obstacles. English and its statistics reside in the human brain, and they can be tapped at the source. One has only to show a list of the latest three words of a passage to a person unfamiliar with those preceding and ask him to make up a sentence including these three words and to write down the word which, in that sentence, follows the three. The statistics linking four-word combinations are automatically evoked in this process. The word chosen *can* and *is likely to* follow the three. There is, however, a chance element in the choice. The word chosen is not *determined* by the preceding three words, for different people, or the same person at different times, would choose a different word.

In following this procedure we can also, without added difficulty, include punctuation and capitalization. This further lends naturalness to the result.

Starting with the words, "When the morning—" I obtained from twenty-one acquaintances:

"When the morning broke after an orgy of abandon he said her head shook quickly vertically aligned in a sequence of words follows what"

This begins well, and the eighteen words following the initial three have a clear meaning. Afterwards there is a wandering of the mind, as in some cases of schizophrenia.[1] But whose is the meaning, and whose mind wanders? We must admit that the meaning exists only in the minds of the readers. Each of the twenty-one writers knew only four words, and each thought of them in a different context. There was no "meaning" until someone read the completed passage. And there was no wandering of the mind, but only failure of such short-range statistics as were taken into account to hold the text together over many words. The words are connected to those immediately preceding them, but have no connection with those further ahead. I think, however, that it is the seeming sense of the passage and not its long-range incoherence that is astounding. And, it is a little disturbing to think that an elaborate machine, taking longer-range statistics into account, would have done still better. The passage seems to us to have meaning, and yet the true and only source of this quotation is a small part of the statistics of the English language—and chance.

Presumably, written English is coherent over long stretches, when it is, because of some overriding purpose in the writer's mind. Or, is it coherent because the writer is unconsciously constructing his text to obey certain long-range statistical rules? And, we wonder, how many times does a person let his pen or tongue, started by some initial impetus, merely run through a sequence of probable words?

This sort of investigation became interesting for its own sake. A couple of hours spent in a conference room with two mathematicians and two engineers produced a half dozen curious forty-word bits. It is scarcely worthwhile to quote the whole of these, but some selected sentences may be of interest:

"When cooked asparagus has a delicious flavor suggesting apples."

"No man should judge his actions by his wife Susie."

"It happened one frosty look of trees waving gracefully against the wall."

We see that the statistics involved are sufficient to give "meaning" frequently, but are scarcely adequate to insure "truth." But, if we mean by "truth" merely that which we are likely to find written in encyclopedias, statistics could presumably supply it, too. However, with the statistics which we have included, any merit of such compositions is more apt to be aesthetic than factual. The last sentence has, for instance, a rather pleasing twisting effect which might have escaped a conscious artist.

We are reminded that philosophers have argued for years about how much of art lies in the work of the artist and how much lies in the observer. I do not know whether or not Dr. Shannon had anything of this in mind, but these consequences of his work certainly have an interesting bearing on the matter. Here there is no creator or "artist." The structure of the words is based merely on statistics, or on the likelihood of their occurring in a certain order. Yet they may have "meaning" for the reader, and he may have an aesthetic appreciation of them.

The passages quoted above were rather disconnected. Our interest finally led us to try a drastic and unscientific experiment. If lack of long-range connection was the chief trouble with the text, we could remedy that. On the bottoms of the slips of paper on which we wrote the words, in plain sight of all, various subjects were indicated, among them *salaries, murder story,* and *women.*

The statement on *salaries* is of interest for a certain partisanship:

"Money isn't everything. However, we need considerably more incentive to produce efficiently. On the other hand too little and too late to suggest a raise without reason for remuneration obviously less than they need although they really are extremely meager."

The *murder story* slip contained a passage which goes a little beyond the bloodiest and most disconnected of the genre:

"When I killed her I stabbed Paul between his powerful jaws clamped tightly together. Screaming loudly despite fatal consequences in the struggle for life began ebbing as he coughed hollowly spitting blood from his ears."

It was on the final slip, *women,* that chance really spoke through clearly. The forty-two word statement is succinct but not entirely quotable. The last sentence says a great deal:

"Some men repeat past mistakes again and again and again."

Perhaps this adage appeared because it has so likely a connection with any part of our lives, our scientific interests included.

NOTE

[1] I quote from Menninger's *The Human Mind,* third edition, page 233: "Have just been to supper. Did not knowing what the woodchuck sent me here. How when the blue blue blue on the said anyone can do it—?"

Science for Art's Sake[*]

IT would seem odd if mathematics had nothing to contribute to the arts, and yet I think that its contribution has been small. Many mathematicians have constructed designs in the forms of well- or little-known mathematical curves. These are often pleasing but never very surprising. An eminent mathematician, George D. Birkhoff, wrote a book on aesthetic measure. To me personally the work seems doubtfully founded in that it looks rather at pieces of porcelain and scraps of paper than at the human beings who appreciate them. As far as creation goes, we need not argue about the methods. The author gives an example to illustrate the application of the rules derived in writing a poem. We see at once that a second-rate poet is, as an artist, still far ahead of a very eminent mathematician. A later author, J. Schillinger, claims a share of the merit of *Porgy and Bess* for his mathematical system of composition. A skeptic might argue that a composer of genius can make a good thing of anything. Certainly, when mathematics is used merely as a sort of guide or crutch, it is hard to apportion credit between the mathematics and the user.

Despite the record, one is inclined to believe that mathematics may be of some real use in connection with the arts, and that it is perhaps through a combination of over-expectancy and misdirection that past users of mathematics have had such dubious success.

The matter of over-expectancy is, I think, very obvious. Scientists do not dash off books giving a world system of science after a few years of work, or even after many. The typical major contribution of the mathematician or physicist is a short paper presenting some new law or proof. Even though a law or theorem may be very general in its implications and applications, the implications and applications

* Reprinted by permission of John R. Pierce from *Astounding Science Fiction* (now *Analog Science Fiction–Science Fact*), November, 1950; copyright © 1950, by Street & Smith Publications, Inc.

are commonly worked out over a good many years by a good many people. It is true that scientific books of great scope are written, but these include much which summarizes the sound work of others, and even these books of wide scope are exceedingly narrow compared, for instance, with a philosophical system of aesthetics or of anything else.

On the contrary, those who wish to apply mathematics to aesthetics seem to feel that they must conquer much at once, and that they must defend to the death their conquests. A combination of attempted universality and solemnity sets a poor atmosphere for investigation.

One should be happy to achieve anything new through mathematics, however narrow the achievement may be. While great art may sometimes be solemn, there is also an art to escape and amusement. Is it too frivolous to suggest that one might enjoy mathematically produced double-talk, even if he cannot have a mathematically produced *Paradise Lost?* The first airplane was none the less wonderful because it could not imitate the grace and endurance of a bird. The automobile is useful even though it cannot think or climb a tree. I believe that the mathematical aesthetician must be content with what he can get and must not ask an infant science to duplicate the achievements of an old race.

This leads at once to the question of aim in applying mathematics to the arts. In the past, the machine has not duplicated the complex abilities of man even in any one narrow field, but rather has done a specific task better than man, or has done something beyond man's power. What, then, could be done by means of mathematics and, perhaps, modern computing machinery, that unaided man finds difficult or impossible? The most common answer is that mathematics can put a pattern into art. From this we have curves and sequences of numbers as a basis for design and music. But perhaps mathematicians can best be used for quite the opposite purpose, that of taking some of the pattern out of art.

It is clear that one thing which human beings find it almost impossible to do is to behave unpredictably in the simple matters of life. One may, for instance, ask a man to produce a random sequence of digits. Statistical studies of such sequences have shown that they are anything but random; it is beyond human power to write down a sequence of numbers which are not in some manner weighted or connected. Tables of random numbers—there are such tables—must be made up by other means and with great care.

In the same way, it is easy to agree that a truly bad poet never, or almost never, writes a good line. One might think that a good line would appear occasionally by chance. The trouble is, chance has no chance to operate. The bad poet is simply too predictable. Cliché follows cliché; love rhymes with dove, and the narrow pattern is dreadfully monotonous. There is nothing new; there is no surprise.

It would be foolish to maintain that surprise is the only feature, or even a main feature of art, but it is an important feature, and it appears in many surprising places. We certainly are amused when Pepys speaks of "my wife, poor wretch." This may have had no element of surprise in the eighteenth century, but it has novelty for us. And it is certain that lack of surprise is a conspicuous element in much inferior art.

Now nothing is more surprising than the number produced by an honest throw of dice. However, the bare numbers turned up have no purely aesthetic interest. It is clear that something else must be added to mere surprise in order to produce anything with amusement value. A clue to what may be added lies in something I discussed in the previous article, "Chance Remarks," something which was based on work that has now appeared in book form as *The Mathematical Theory of Communication,* by Claude E. Shannon and Warren Weaver. This work shows how the missing element can be added to mere randomness.

We have, then, a way of making patterns of letters and words by chance, such patterns as can be aesthetically appreciated by the creative reader. The patterns resemble English words, in that they embody some of the statistics of English. Yet, they escape the more complete predictability of direct constructions of the human mind. In these words the predictable element is carefully, mathematically controlled, so that only so much, of such a kind, and neither more nor less, enters into the process of construction. Just enough structure can be put in to give the words aesthetic value to the reader, while one can stop short of banality.

One may object that these results are meager, and what else should they be at this stage? One may object that they are not new. Indeed, we are reminded of the word frame which the professor showed to Captain Lemuel Gulliver at the Grand Academy of Lagoda. One can only admit that Swift had the general idea first, but that he may have been wrong in rejecting it summarily.

Some examples of stochastic English were given in "Chance Remarks." For a full appreciation of his capacities for creative artistic enjoyment, the reader will need more, however, and some follow. If no title is given, none was written on the bottom of the slip:

1. This was the first. The second time it happened without his approval. Nevertheless it cannot be done. It could hardly have been the only living veteran of the foreign power had stated that never more could happen. Consequently, people seldom try it.

2. John now disported a fine new hat. I paid plenty for the food. When cooked asparagus has a delicious flavor suggesting apples. If anyone wants my wife or any other physicist would not believe my own eyes. I would believe my own word.

3. That was a relief whenever you let your mind go free who knows if that pork chop I took with my cup of tea after was quite good with the heat I couldn't smell anything off it I'm sure that queer looking man in the

4. I forget whether he went on and on. Finally he stipulated that this must stop immediately after this. The last time I saw him when she lived. It happened one frosty look of trees waving gracefully against the wall. You never can

5. McMillan's Theorem

McMillan's theorem states that whenever electrons diffuse in vacua. Conversely inpurities of a cathode. No substitution of variables in the equation relating these quantities. Functions relating hypergeometric series with confluent terms converging to limits uniformly expanding rationally to represent any function.

6. House Cleaning

First empty the furniture of the master bedroom and bath. Toilets are to be washed after polishing doorknobs the rest of the room. Washing windows semiannually is to be taken by small aids such as husbands are prone to omit soap powder.

7. Epaminondas

Epaminondas was one who was powerful especially on land and sea. He was the leader of great fleet maneuvers and open sea battles against Pelopidas but had been struck on the head during the second Punic war because of the wreck of an armored frigate.

I believe that few people will read this material without some interest or amusement. Is this not enough justification in calling it a contribution of mathematics to the arts?

While interest and enjoyment are clearly the contribution of the reader, the reader will be interested and will enjoy only if the text is (1) recognizable in part at least as possible sequences of words, and (2) original. Thus, consider "It happened one frosty look of trees waving gracefully against the wall." We realize that someone might say this, or, even, might want to say it. However, a person's habits are so strong as to make him unlikely to say it. Starting with the first three words, most people would have said something different and more common. The simple process by which the sentence was constructed has no such inhibitions. As a matter of fact, some people—madmen and great artists—don't have many. In case the reader has not suspected it already, numbers 3 and 7 are not statistical English. Number 3 is from James Joyce's *Ulysses* and number 7 from the writings of a schizophrenic.

Perhaps the best means for further exploration is the application of similar means in a different field of art. In the field of visual art one finds himself anticipated by the kaleidoscope, which combines a random arrangement of colored fragments into a sixfold geometric pattern—a simple example of much the sort of thing we have been considering. We may remember, too, that many years ago Marcel Duchamps allowed a number of threads to fall on pieces of cloth and then framed and preserved them. Our example shall be in the field of music.

In order to construct music by a stochastic process, a catalog of allowed chords on roots 1-6 in the key of C was made. Actually, it was necessary to make a catalog of root 1 chords only: the others could be derived. By the throwing of three especially made dice and by the use of a table of random numbers, one chord was chosen to follow another. The only rule of connection was that two succeeding chords have a common tone in the same voice. Each composition consisted of eight measures of four quarter notes each. In order to give some pattern, measures 5 and 6 repeat measures 1 and 2. In addition, it was specified that chords 1, 16, and 32 have root 1, and that chords 15 and 31 have either root 4 or root 5.

Three statistical pieces were rapidly constructed according to these rules. Each took perhaps half a day. They are reproduced here so that the curious may play them.

I asked an experienced pianist to play these three for me several times. After a few repetitions, he came to add a certain amount of phrasing and expression which he felt natural. Thus, he made a performer's contribution to these works of art. Certainly one cannot

RANDOM I

RANDOM II

RANDOM III

object that he was violating the intentions of the composer.

What about the listener's contribution? In my case, I found the pieces a little meaningless at first, but after I had heard them several times and could recognize them, they became more "comprehensible." Acting in the capacity of a music critic, I should say that they are pleasing rather than deep. They are less dull than poor hymns but are considerably inferior to Bach.

From their common characteristics the pieces are clearly products of the same composer. Some identifying features are that voices tend either to stick to one note repeatedly or to jump wildly. Too, many "laws" of harmony—no parallel fifths, no doubling of the leading tone, and so on—are flagrantly ignored.

No doubt, by use of more complicated rules, stochastic music could be produced which would violate fewer of the rules of harmony. But would this result in a gain or a loss? If the process has value, does this value not in some degree come from a lack of prejudice and predictability? Statistical music should be urged toward respectability only with caution.

In this connection it is quite possible that such statistical methods could be of use in trying out proposed systems of harmony. It is difficult for a musician easily to follow new rules; a statistical process is indifferent to whether the rules incorporated in it are old and well known or new and untried.

Returning to the examples of music given, one may object that the three pieces are unduly simple rhythmically and are too conventional harmonically. For the lover of modern music I have concocted a dissonant canon in the whole-tone scale. I will not describe the process of construction in detail, beyond saying that, except for the last measure, choices were made by repeatedly throwing one die. I won't say much for the canon beyond the fact that while the statistical structure is such as to give both cohesion and variety, the process of composition was quite simple. Artistically, it is perhaps a severe challenge to the listener's powers of creative appreciation.

How seriously is all this to be taken? I think that the crude material presented shows that short pieces of amusing and enjoyable text and music can be produced by processes which are essentially statistical in their character. The interest of this text and music is clearly dependent both on familiarity and on surprise. The processes could be refined. It is not beyond conjecture that a machine could write murder mysteries, for instance, each one a little different, at the

punch of a button, with *hard-boiled, sex, deduction,* and other styles and features adjusted to the user's individual taste.

All this has, however, raised for me an issue beyond that of the stochastic generation of art. Apparently, if I try hard, I am capable of liking almost anything that is surprising if only it has some order or recognizable feature. Too, I am not entirely alone in this. I wonder how much of the appreciation of some of the more drastic experiments in writing, music, and painting is a combination of a knowledge of the artist's style and tricks and a determined effort to enjoy? How can one tell?

Washington Dateline*

Washington, April 1, 1950

HITLER'S most deadly secret weapon, with which he hoped to the last to win the war, was revealed in Washington today by a Nazi scientist. The weapon is known to the Russians and may be in use in this country.

Dr. Hagen Krankheit told reporters that he had smuggled the secret of the top Nazi weapon into this country. The weapon was known only to himself, two technicians who were executed before the fall of Berlin, Joseph Goebbels, and the Fuehrer himself. Dr. Krankheit gained access to this country after the war in the guise of a rocket engineer. Recently he has been threatened with expulsion as a dangerous alien.

The weapon, known as the "Müllabfuhrwortmaschine," is a complex device for writing propaganda with great flexibility and sublety. In appearance it much resembles a large digital computer much as the ENIAC or the MANIAC, Dr. Krankheit said. A few key words and instructions are put in, and the device automatically produces propaganda in limitless quantity, using all possible combinations and, unlike a human being, overlooking none.

A prominent scientist said that he believed such a machine to be possible, and that it had been partly anticipated in the work of Dr. Norbert Weiner of The Massachusetts Institute of Technology and Dr. Claude Shannon of the Bell Telephone Laboratories. He did not know of any such machine in this country, he said, but admitted that he did not read the papers.

Dr. Krankheit said that the original primitive idea for the

machine had been stolen from the Russians by espionage early in the Nazi regime. He insisted that the German machine was a Nazi development, but admitted that the Russians might be using a similar device. Dr. Krankheit hinted that such a machine might be in operation in this country, but he refused to give particulars.

Although the original machine was of almost infinite complexity, the fundamental principle is simple. Dr. Krankheit demonstrated this with three sets of cards. On one set of cards were written phrases called "entities," on another phrases called "operators," and, on a third, more "entity" phrases. By shuffling each set of cards and dealing out one card from each, propaganda is produced.

Dr. Krankheit demonstrated the cards by producing such statements as:

"Subversive elements were revealed to be related by marriage to a well-known columnist."

"Capitalist warmonger is a weak link in atomic security."

"Atomic scientist is said to be associated with certain religious and racial groups."

The actual machine, Dr. Krankheit revealed, could produce whole pages of propaganda suitable for immediate distribution. This was delivered either in printed form or directly as spoken words interspersed with martial and patriotic music. The machine could be adjusted to associate any group with various favorable or unfavorable groups or qualities in any desired degree. Dr. Krankheit said that the problem of making the output reasonably connected had been solved only after immense labor, but had been made easier by the fact that propaganda does not have to make sense as long as it achieves its objective.

A committee spokesman scouted the idea that there is such a machine in use in this country. He commented in part: "This is an effort by fellow travelers to undermine confidence in the American way of life. We have evidence of a weak link in military security. Government laxness must be called to account. The F.B.I. should investigate all subversive elements."

A Russian spokesman indignantly denied that his country would use such a device. "This is a capitalist warmongering plot," he said. "Russia stands for true democracy. The degraded and beastly tools of Wall Street will defeat themselves." He added that the machine's true inventor was an as yet unnamed Russian scientist.

Artists and Machines*

FROM the earliest days, temples, palaces, and ships have appeared in man's art, together with seas and mountains, animals and human beings. Man's artifacts have been regarded as a part of his world, a part perhaps less alien and better understood than natural objects and creatures.

During and even preceding the industrial revolution, the machine was added to this world of man. Diderot's encyclopedia is full of mills and engines. Artists of the nineteenth century portrayed canals and aqueducts, steamships and locomotives as they would have the grandeur of nature. Poets, including Southey, the Poet Laureate, eulogized engineers as they might have hailed victors in battle. Perhaps not everyone understood the engineering and science behind technology, but not everyone understood the economics, politics, law, or theology which were also part of a familiar and accepted world.

For some, technology and machines are still accepted as a part of man's world, no more alien or unintelligible than its other aspects. Catalytic crackers, no less than funny little locomotives and rural politicians, have a place in Thomas Hart Benton's art. Charles Sheeler has painted factories as another might have painted forests and plains. Any lack of a detailed understanding of technology perturbed these artists no more than ignorance of geology perturbs a landscape painter.

Some artists, however, find the machine alien, as, indeed, some find man's world inhospitable. They represent machines in disjointed fragments, as bones may symbolize a world of the damned or the dead. They evoke from machines meaningless monstrosities as strange as the biological monstrosities of Hieronymus Bosch. They

---

* Reprinted with permission from the Catalog of "Bewogen Beweging," Stedelijk Museum, Amsterdam, March 10–April 17, 1961.

are awed by symbols or parts of machines, as the superstitious are awed by religious signs or by the relics of saints.

These reactions to a part of our world seem to me to be cowardly and irrational. How much better are Rube Goldberg's familiar ribbing of gadgets, however powerful, and Jean Tinguely's use of wheels, motors, and mechanisms to create both transient effects and those more persistent patterns which are pictures.

The gifted inventor need not be learned in science, but some effects can be created only through deep learning. The electronic computer is one of man's tools which can be wielded only with understanding. Yet L. A. Hiller, of the University of Illinois, has made it generate music which contains both imposed pattern and random, surprising features. In the course of work at the Bell Laboratories on what constitutes a visual pattern, Bella Julesz has made a computer produce simple, pleasing patterns with elements of both randomness and order. Also at the Bell Laboratories, M. V. Mathews has made a computer produce various musical sounds of unusual quality. With the RCA music synthesizer, Milton Babbitt and Vladimir Ussachevsky are doing pioneering work at the Columbia University Electronic Music Laboratory. In Holland, France, Germany, Austria, and elsewhere, men who understand science and technology and who love art are using machines with no sense of alienage.

Artists, regard not machines with awe or trepidation! However strange and surprising they may be, they are less so than a man, yea, less so than an ant. Joke about machines, incorporate machines into still life, or bend machines to your purposes, but do not fear, worship, hate, or even mutilate machines. They are beneath man's high estate.

Computer Synthesis of Musical Sounds*

LED by such pioneers as the late Edgard Varèse, during the last quarter century composers have become increasingly interested in extending the resources of music. They have used such sources as oscillators, white noise generators, and pulse generators, rather than directly imitative instruments such as electronic organs and electrical guitars. A large body of this so-called electronic music has been composed and produced at American and European studios, for instance, the Columbia-Princeton Electronic Music Center in New York, the Experimental Music Studio at Urbana, and the Westdeutscher Rundfunk in Cologne; and a great deal of *musique concrète* has been produced by the Groupe des Recherches in Paris. Many of these works are available on tapes and records and are heard with increasing frequency in concert halls. Composers and engineers have developed elaborate techniques for the creative use of those sound resources previously unavailable for musical composition; and, with the help of behavioral scientists and electronic apparatus for synthesizing sound, they have also undertaken psychoacoustic investigations.

The digital computer is a new, powerful and flexible electronic resource, and it was inevitable that an effort should be made to use modern computers in connection with music. Indeed, this has been done with a variety of approaches.

One possible field of use is in the analysis or production of musical scores. I myself dabbled with this idea as far back as 1950[1] and others have pursued the matter far more diligently. Accounts of such work and bibliographies concerning it can be found in recent articles by Lejaren Hiller and James Beauchamp[2] and by J. R. Pierce, M. V. Mathews and J.-C. Risset.[3]

* Reprinted from *The Rockefeller University Review,* November, 1965, with the permission of The Rockefeller University Press; copyright © 1966, by The Rockefeller University Press.

Some five years ago, M. V. Mathews, N. Guttman, and I found a quite different application for the computer in connection with music. This was not in the analysis or composition of music, but in the production of musical sounds.

We were led into this by the use of the digital computer at the Bell Laboratories as a means for simulating the performance of complex speech processing devices, such a vocoders. In such simulation, the speech is reduced to a numerical description. This description is then processed by the computer as the original speech wave would be processed by the device simulated. The computer produces a sequence of numbers which represent the output of the device, and this sequence of numbers is recorded on magnetic tape and then converted into sound.

It is easy to go from this use of the computer to the idea of having the computer produce by prescribed rule a sequence of numbers to be converted into the corresponding sound. This is what we did. Our work has been described in a number of publications.[4,5]

The computer is an interesting source of sound, whether the sound be synthetic speech (toward which we are working) or sounds which might be used in music. For the computer is a universal source of sound, without any of the specialization of the human voice or of musical instruments, either mechanical or electronic. A mathematical theorem, called the sampling theorem, tells us that if a musical or other sound contains no frequencies above the frequency B, the sound can be accurately and completely represented by and re-created from a series of $2B$ numbers per second, numbers which describe the amplitude of the sound wave at equally spaced *sampling times*.

Thus, if we want to use the computer to generate sound waves with frequencies no higher than 5,000 cycles per second, we cause the computer to write 10,000 numbers per second on a magnetic tape. In order to produce a sound wave, these numbers are read out through a digital-to-analog converter. When the resulting sequence of pulses is passed through a low-pass filter whose bandwidth is 5,000 cycles per second, the output will be a smooth wave, representing the sound. What numbers do we cause the computer to write? We program the computer to choose the numbers according to some rule; for instance, a very simple rule might be that the samples be ordinates of a sine wave of specified frequency and amplitude. We can go beyond this to other wave forms and to more complicated specifications.

Let me emphasize the universality of the computer. It can in principle produce any sound, not only any hearable sound, but any possible sound of limited bandwidth, whether or not the ear can distinguish that sound from other sounds.

Compared with this potential universality, the sounds we actually have produced cover a comparatively narrow range. Yet these sounds have seemed to us to have interesting, or we might say musical, qualities. The range of sounds produced overlaps the range of conventional musical sounds. The computer sounds exhibit some features which are not found in conventional music and, alas, conventional music exhibits many desirable features which we have not been able to produce by means of the computer.

Our procedure has been to generate various sounds and present them in simple man-made musical compositions. Just hearing a sound once is insufficient for us to make a judgment concerning it. Repeating a sound indefinitely is boring. Thus, we have felt that in exploring sounds it is best to put them in some simple, short, musical context. Many of our experiments are available on a Decca record, "Music from Mathematics." [6]

The examples given on the record are arranged in a rather arbitrary order, which somewhat obscures the progress we have made and how we were led from one thing to another. I propose to recapitulate some of the successive steps we took in attaining a greater variety and better quality of sound.

In a very early piece called "Stochatta," the musical sounds were merely sine waves and squarish waves, which were turned on and off abruptly. There was a little more flexibility than in the electronic organ in that the amplitudes of the sounds could be chosen at will and very complex rhythmic patterns could be easily produced, but in other respects the sounds of "Stochatta" are much more primitive than those of a good electronic organ.

We of course knew very well from musical lore that variations of amplitude and frequency with time are extremely important. We surmised that an abrupt rise and gradual fall in the amplitude of a wave would give the sound a plucked quality, and that a small sinusoidal variation in frequency would add the pleasantness or warmth associated with vibrato. The validity of these conjectures is demonstrated in a short piece called "Variations in Timbre and Attack." This piece also exhibits a peculiar slurring quality associated with an abrupt frequency shift near the beginning of a note. In this piece a simple melody is played in the first three sections, but in the fourth section two quite different sequences of pure sinusoidal tones are played. However, the *difference* between the frequencies of the two simultaneous tones is always the frequency of a note of the original simple melody. And, it is the original melody that the listener hears.

There are some effects which are very difficult, if not impossible, to achieve with conventional instruments. One is an extensive or very rapid portamento—a smooth shift in frequency during the playing of a note. Another is the use of scales with arbitrary numbers of notes per octave. An early piece by M. V. Mathews, called "Numerology," exhibits both of these. In this composition a very rapid portamento in a high register gives a chirping sound. Part of the composition is written in a ten-tone equally tempered scale.

It is easy to make the computer generate pseudorandom noise. Indeed, one can generate noise with various bandwidths, and one can impose noise on periodic waves, either by adding it to the wave forms or by using the noise to modulate the amplitude or the frequency of the wave. This makes it possible to produce sounds which range from periodic to completely noisy. But because they are band limited around some central frequency, even the noisy sounds can have, if not a precise pitch, at least the quality of being high or low in pitch. Some of the potentialities of a mixture of periodic and noisy sounds are realized in a piece by M. V. Mathews, "The Second Law," and in "Noise Study," by J. C. Tenney.

Thus, at first our course was to follow a conjecture that some feature, such as wave form, or vibrato, or attack, or randomness, would have roughly predictable and musically interesting subjective effects. This led us through a considerable range of sensation. Some things, however, eluded us. For instance, we have not yet produced anything with the sense of fullness of an orchestra or a choir of instruments. At one time we believed that adding a little randomness to sounds would produce this effect, but although a small amount of randomness does make a sound a little richer, we have never attained the sensation of many instruments, and we now know that increasing the randomness in simple ways merely makes the sound noisy.

Another frustrating thing is that although we produced sounds which seemed "plucked"—like those made by guitar, mandolin, or harpsichord—and sounds that were fluty and recorder-like and reedy, we stumbled upon no violin-like sounds or brasslike sound. This led us to believe that it would be necessary to examine the sounds of orchestral instruments very closely to see if there were simple physical features of the wave form which would enable us to attain a wider variety of timbres without outright imitation.

We had reason to believe that this approach might be profitable. For instance, H. Fletcher, E. Donnell Blackham, and Richard Stratton[7] had shown that the warmth of piano tones, especially in the lower register, is associated with the fact that the overtones are not strictly harmonic, but lie above the harmonic frequencies because of the stiffness of the strings. At the Bell Laboratories J. C. Tenney, in studying bell sounds, confirmed the well-known fact that overtones far from harmonic frequencies give a harsh bell sound. He also found, however, that if the overtones are exactly harmonic the sound is not like that of a bell at all and is, indeed, much less interesting.

In 1964, J. C. Tenney, who had been at the Bell Laboratories for two years, went to the Yale School of Music. He was given a National Science Foundation grant to study the relation between objective features of sound-wave forms and their subjective correlates. His aim was to discover what features of sound waves are important to the musical quality of a sound, and what features are irrelevant or unimportant. He has studied violin sounds intensively by means of computer harmonic analysis of successive pitch periods.

Helmholtz held that a moving violin bow grips the string and holds it until the original disturbance of the string by the bow travels as a wave up to the end of the string near the nut, is reflected, and returns to the bow. Tenney's work indicates that this theory is faulty, and that the bow releases the string sooner than Helmholtz asserted. Tenney found that every third harmonic is weak in the upper range of violin sounds. This indicates that the string moves with the bow for about two-thirds of a cycle. Further, the deletion of harmonics which are multiples of three tends to impart a violin-like or cello-like quality to computer-generated sound.

In 1964, J.-C. Risset, a young French physicist with considerable musical training and insight, came to the Bell Laboratories for a year. During that period he worked on the analysis and synthesis of trumpet sounds. He found that a number of factors are extremely important. One is that the overtones rise later but more rapidly than the fundamental. Another is that the overtones are stronger relative to the fundamental in loud trumpet sounds than in soft trumpet sounds. This is reminiscent of the fact that the overtones are stronger in a loud or shouting voice than at normal conversational level—the reason television commercials remain insistent even when we turn the volume down. Risset was so successful in synthesizing trumpet sounds that trained musicians are unable to distinguish the synthesized from the natural sounds with better than chance accuracy.

Other examples indicate how it is possible to increase the variety of computer-produced sounds. For instance, R. N. Shepard has produced sounds in sequence which seem to rise in pitch, step by step, yet which never in fact leave the octave.[8]

To the musician, and especially to the composer, the computer offers an instrument for sound production which is in principle infinitely flexible, though the exploitation of this flexibility calls for considerable knowledge and insight. The computer has no inherent scales, harmonic intervals, or timbres, and no limitations of rhythm, tempo, or dynamics—the composer can choose freely, accepting or rejecting tradition in any degree. But if a composer is to use a computer, he can no longer call on the instrument maker or the performing artist for help. If he wants notes or intervals outside of a traditional scale, he must specify what frequencies he wants. If he wants a particular sound quality, he must supply the computer with an objective description of a wave form which will give the desired psychoacoustic effect. If he wants to achieve expressive effects through legato, staccato, crescendo, or ritardando, he must put these into his instructions to the computer. Yet the result may eventually be worth the difficulty. And, by assuming these responsibilities, a composer can potentially go beyond the capabilities of any instruments or of any performers. Here is a challenge to composers, old and young, to master a new musical language in order to make use of a new mode of expression.

To the student of music the computer, with careful psychoacoustic experimentation, makes it possible to attack many problems experimentally which have in the past been approached chiefly "philosophically," that is, with heated debate and disagreement. The way of science is not to seek agreement on arbitrary questions, but to discover in what range of experience we are forced into agreement by experiments which can be replicated. I think that psychoacoustics, together with the computer, can put us on firmer ground in a number of respects.

Some aspects of the question as to what "rules" of music should be attributed to acculturation and what to the nature of the human being—to the limitations and capabilities of his hearing and to his ability to remember sequences of sounds—are certainly amenable to experiment. Indeed, recent experiments by R. Plomp and W. J. M. Levelt[9] seem to me to show the inescapability of Helmholtz's theory that consonant intervals are those in which the harmonics of the two tones coincide or are adequately separated in frequency. Moreover, this work casts further light on the question of consonance.

The use of the computer in producing with great ease accurate tonal and rhythmic patterns opens the way to all sorts of interesting investigations. Among these could be whether the procedures of twelve-tone composition do give an acoustic as well as a numerical unity to compositions. In plainer terms, is the sort of orderliness that twelve-tone composers introduce into their compositions apparent to the listener? (The fact that music judged as good is orderly does not imply that music which is orderly need be judged as good.)

Whatever computer generation of musical sounds can mean to composers and to students of music, it is pertinent to my work for what it means to the science and technology of acoustics. Sound quality and the problems of understanding vocal sounds and generating high-quality artificial speech are all central to communication. To arrive at an understanding of the quality of sounds calls not only for sharp minds, but for sharp ears. I feel that a strong effort on the part of musicians in the understanding and synthesis of good musical sounds will be invaluable to psychoacoustics in other fields, including that of communication.

NOTES

[1] J. J. Coupling, "Science for Art's Sake," *Astounding Science Fiction*, November, 1950.

[2] Lejaren Hiller and James Beauchamp, "Research in Music with Electronics," *Science,* Vol. 150, No. 3692 (1955), 161-69.

[3] J. R. Pierce, M. V. Mathews, and J.-C. Risset, "Further Experiments on the Use of the Computer in Connection with Music," *Gravesaner Blätter,* No. 27/28, November, 1965, 92–97.

[4] M. V. Mathews, "The Digital Computer as a Musical Instrument," *Science,* Vol. 142, No. 3592 (1963), 555-57.

[5] J. R. Pierce, "Portrait of the Machine as a Young Artist," *Playboy,* Vol. 12, No. 6 (1965), 124-25, 150, 182, 184.

[6] "Music from Mathematics," Decca Record DL9103 (monaural) or DL79103 (binaural).

[7] H. Fletcher, E. Donnell Blackham, and Richard Stratton, "Quality of Piano Tones," *Journal of the Acoustical Society of America,* Vol. 34, No. 6 (1962), 749-61.

[8] R. N. Shepard, "Circularity of Judgments of Relative Pitch," *ibid.,* Vol. 12, No. 36 (1964), 2346-53.

[9] R. Plomp and W. J. M. Levelt, "Tonal Consonance and Critical Bandwidth," *ibid.,* Vol. 38, No. 4 (1965), 548-60.

Portrait of the Machine as a Young Artist*

TWO reproductions of prints by Harunobu hang on the right wall of my office. I know what I think of these. On the left I have reproductions of paintings by Ingres and David. I know what I think of these, too. When I look at the wall opposite my desk, I am a little puzzled. There I see a buff painting, five feet long and ten and a half inches wide. I understand the inscription in the lower left; it reads: *Pour John Pierce, amicalement, Jean Tinguely, Avril 1962.*

The painting itself consists of strokes of red, turquoise, and gray ink, generally to the right and downward. Most of the strokes are accented at the beginning. The pattern of strokes is densest and widest a little above the middle, and the turquoise and gray strokes are nearly vertical toward the bottom of the picture. The general effect is Japanese.

This painting is the product of a stupid machine of clanking metal parts, a machine devised and built by the talented constructor of the jiggling "metametics" which have been shown in many countries, and of the celebrated "self-destroying machine" which partially succeeded some years ago in the courtyard of the Museum of Modern Art. Tinguely once built many painting machines similar to the one that created my picture, and sold them to a variety of people, including Nelson Rockefeller.

If I didn't like the painting on my wall, I wouldn't have it there. I am astonished that in some sense it is the product of a machine. But I am appalled when I think that a few hundred feet to my left there resides a machine, an electronic computer, which is to Tinguely's machine as Newton is to an earthworm. What sort of art can we expect from a comparative genius of a machine when a clanking metal monstrosity can produce a picture of at least dubious merit?

While intellectual visionaries have busied themselves asserting that the computer will outstrip man in his intellectual endeavors, and will manage wisely where the executive now mismanages, a less noisy few have approached the computer with artistic intentions, hoping to elicit from it something more patterned and of greater impact than chaos.

Indeed, a similar quest goes back well beyond the digital computer. Many years ago, Marcel Duchamp, who painted *Nude Descending a Staircase,* allowed one-meter-long white threads to fall from a height of one meter upon a flat surface. Some were framed and I have seen them. In the curved order imposed by the stiffness of the thread and the random configuration resulting from its passage through the air, there is a mixture of the graceful and the unexpected. Too, by adding a repeated symmetry to a random pattern of bits of colored glass, the kaleidoscope has pleased many generations of children and adults.

From the remote past to the very present, human beings have *incorporated* geometrical forms and psychological tricks in their art. The straight lines and rectangles of Mondrian have a geometrical regularity which we might associate with a machine, and the subtle curves of Op Art remind us both of mathematical curves and of the psychological texts on perception and optical illusions from which they are drawn. When the artist approaches science and the machine, will the machine perhaps approach the complexity and surprise which we associate with the human artist?

I don't know who first used the electronic computer to produce patterns of some originality and interest, but it may have been Dr. Bela Julesz of the Bell Telephone Laboratories. In studying properties of vision, Dr. Julesz caused the computer to generate patterns of black and white dots within squares, in which just a little order was imposed upon randomness. The result was so pleasing that a Japanese publisher used the pattern on the cover of a translation of the book in which it appeared.

Others have invoked the computer as an artist with more direct motives. Thus, the computer has been used not only to solve the equations of motion of a particular kind of satellite in orbit around the earth, but also to create an animated motion picture showing the satellite at first tumbling around in its orbit and finally aligning itself radially so that it points at the earth. Another programmer has caused the computer to produce a whole animated instructional motion picture showing rolling balls, the operation of the computer itself, and titles that rise across the screen expand, and dissolve. The result is far from Walt Disney in skill, but much cheaper in cost. And one ingenious programmer did manage to make the computer draw pictures of Mickey Mouse's head as seen from any chosen direction.

This is serious work. Scientists and engineers want to present data in graphical and even in moving form, and they want to see what proposed devices and structures will look like from various angles. In some cases, the computer can produce the required drawings, or sequences of drawings, much more quickly and cheaply than could the most skilled draftsman.

But people have been tempted beyond these practical essays in computer art. In fact, one ingenious man, A. M. Noll, caused the computer to generate drawings in the style of Piet Mondrian, drawings consisting of short, heavy vertical and horizontal lines rather randomly arranged on a sheet of paper. Then Noll carried out a psychological experiment. He showed 100 people an original Mondrian drawing and a drawing made by the computer in the style of Mondrian. He asked them to decide which drawing was artistically better, and which was produced by a machine. Of all those asked, only 28 percent correctly identified the computer picture, and 59 percent preferred it to the Mondrian. However, people who said they disliked or were indifferent to modern art were equally divided in preferring the computer picture or the Mondrian; but people who said they liked modern art preferred the computer picture three to one. I don't know whether this is overestimating the computer's artistic ability or underestimating Mondrian's.

Noll has taken the computer far beyond imitation. In his use of the computer, he always prescribes some order but leaves the drawing partly to chance. By these means he has produced a weaving pattern formed by a self-intersecting line, patterns of lines splattered over a page, and even pairs of drawings which, when viewed through a stereoscope, give the effect of many lines hanging in space, much like the *Orpheus and Apollo* of Richard Lippold in the foyer of the Philharmonic Hall in Lincoln Center in New York City, but without any supporting wires at all. I feel driven to the fatuous comment: It's fascinating, but is it *art*?

Whether the computer, man, or both together create the art of the future, it is likely that man rather than the computer will enjoy it, and the place of a good deal of art is in the home. Today we have books and magazines, TV, slides, and primitive forms of 3-D. But the future holds something better in store for us. Emmet Leith and his colleagues at the University of Michigan have produced a visual effect as real as looking through a window.

By illuminating an object to be "photographed" with a coherent beam of light from a laser, that much-vaunted marvel of quantum electronics, Leith produces what is called a hologram, a wavy pattern of ultrafine lines on a photographic plate. When this hologram is illuminated by a laser, a person looking through it sees behind the hologram what appears to be a very solid three-dimensional version of the object that was used in producing the hologram. The whole object is represented in all parts of the hologram. When one moves his head, it is just as if he were looking through a window. If a less interesting detail is in front of an interesting part of the object, one merely has to move his head to see around it. Imagine such solidity, such rotundity, which goes far beyond that of 3-D movies or the old-fashioned stereoscope. At present, one can achieve this effect in only one color, and in still pictures, but who knows what the future will bring?

A computer is blind, deaf, and dumb, and it produces visual art only because someone forces it to. A computer can just as well produce a numerical description of a sound wave—in fact, a description of any sound wave. Don't think that people who are ear-minded rather than eye-minded have neglected to make computers produce sound. In the earliest attempts, a computer was made to play simple tunes in buzzes or squeaks, but we are now far beyond that point. A Decca record of 1962, *Music from Mathematics,* shows that the computer can play tunes in a variety of tone qualities, imitating plucked strings, reed instruments and other common effects, and going beyond these to produce shushes, garbles, and clunks that are unknown in conventional music. Further, the computer can even speak and sing. In the record I refer to, the computer actually sings *A Bicycle Built for Two*—to its own accompaniment.

Today, scientists and musicians at Massachusetts Institute of Technology, Bell Telephone Laboratories, Princeton University, and the Argonne National Laboratory are trying to make the computer play and sing more surprisingly and more mellifluously. As a musical instrument, the computer has unlimited potentialities for uttering sound. It can, in fact, produce strings of numbers representing any conceivable or hearable sound. But as yet, the programmers are somewhat in the position of a savage confronted with the grand piano. Wonderful things could come out of that box if only we knew how to evoke them.

While some mathematical musicians, and musical mathematicians, are trying to use a computer as a super orchestra, others are following a much older line of endeavor, which goes back to Mozart. Mozart provided posterity with a collection of assorted numbered bars in three-eight time together with a set of rules. By throwing dice to obtain a sequence of random numbers, and by using these numbers in choosing successive bars according to simple rules, even the nonmusical amateur can "compose" an almost endless number of little waltzes, which sound something like disorganized Mozart. Joseph Haydn, Maximilian Stadler, and Carl Philipp Emanuel Bach are said to have produced similar random music.

In more recent times, the inimitable John Cage has used a random process in the selection of notes. Indeed, there is a whole school who believe that chance is better than judgment and that a composition would be freshest if the composer guided it in a general way only, letting the individual notes fall where they will.

Some of the early experiments in this direction were as primitive as shaking a pen at a sheet of music paper and adding stems to the ink dots. Since the coming of the computer, chaos has entered music more scientifically. In 1956, the Burroughs Corporation announced it had used the computer to generate music, and in 1957 it was announced that Dr. Martin Kline and Dr. Douglas Bolitho had used the Datatron to write popular melodies. Jack Owens set words to one—which was played over the ABC network as Pushbutton Bertha. In 1957, F. P. Brooks, Jr., A. L. Hopkins, Jr., P. G. Neumann, and W. V. Wright published an account of the statistical composition of music on the basis of extensive statistical data on hymn tunes.

Perhaps the most ambitious early attempt was that of Lejaren A. Hiller, Jr., and Leonard M. Isaacson of the University of Illinois, who succeeded in formulating the rules of four-part first-species counterpoint in such a way that a computer could choose notes randomly and reject them if they violated these rules. Music so generated, together with other partially random, partially controlled music, was published in 1957 as the *Illiac Suite for the String Quartet.*

Since that time, the computer has come to function in a dual capacity, as an orchestra playing its own compositions. J. C. Tenney, who is now in the music department at Yale, has been a strong advocate of this approach. As a composer, he provides general guidance to the computer as to high or low, slow or fast, loud or soft, and some guidance as to timbre. Within specified ranges that change with time, the computer chooses the notes at random and plays them according to its own directions. The results are surprising in many ways. However unpredictable chance may be, it has a sort of uniformity that seems to preclude the kind of surprise one finds in Haydn's *Surprise Symphony,* that is, a carefully calculated loud effect following a soft passage. Perhaps the composer should provide the computer with more or less guidance, or perhaps guidance should be built into the computer.

Musicians of the modern school condemn, or at least wish to depart from, traditional musical devices and forms, but this hasn't kept musical scholars from analyzing music to see just what the form consists of. Harry F. Olson and his co-workers at RCA have already put Stephen Foster's melodies through the wringer and caused a computer to generate Foster-like tunes. In principle, what makes Mozart like Mozart, Haydn like Haydn, Wagner like Wagner is not beyond analysis. I would be very surprised if someone could cause a computer to produce good and original Mozart at the push of a button. I wouldn't be surprised at someone's making the computer sound something like Haydn or Mozart or Bach.

As in the case of the visual arts, new science and technology have much to offer in the reproduction as well as in the creation of the sounds of the future. It's a commonplace that listening to a stereo system, however good, isn't like hearing an orchestra in a concert hall. Yet it is not beyond the ability of science to create in one very particular place in a room the exact environment of sound that one would experience in a concert hall. Manfred Schroeder at the Bell Telephone Laboratories has shown how this can be done. He uses the computer to process the sounds that will be played over a pair of loudspeakers, so that in the vicinity of a person's head he creates the exact acoustical environment of a huge reverberant hall. This effect is uncanny. It is much fuller than a stereo system, and it is very different from hearing something through headphones.

The ability to localize sounds outside one's head, the feeling of being immersed in sound, depends on the way in which what one hears changes as he moves his head slightly. Schroeder cleverly simulates the sound near the head so that when one turns his head slightly, this has just the effect on the sounds he hears that it would if he were in an auditorium. At present this has to be carried out at great cost in an anechoic or echoless chamber, a large and expensive room with sound-absorbing walls. But who is to say that at some not-distant date it may not be possible to create exactly the same effect in any easy chair at home?

The question of whether a computer can be made to *write* as well as to draw, compose, and play is no less provocative. The manufacture of *meaningful* prose and poetry, as of art and music, is a challenge that may or may not be beyond the capacity of the computer, but the composition of striking new words and sentences is certainly well within the realm of mechanization. As part of a linguistic experiment conducted at the Bell Telephone Laboratories in 1961, for example, Dr. Melvin Hinich caused a computer to generate a number of rather compelling sentences which, considered as a single composition, might be said to substantiate my belief that the artistic utterances of mechanical chance and of contemporary avant-garde writers are approaching each other so closely as to come into competition. Wrote the computer.

this is shooting
this seems to be sleeping
a vapid ruby with a nutty fan lies seldom below this tipsy noise.
   this cute snake by that wet pig is clawing coolly to a weak pig
any black otter below a holy fan is poking hotly in that furry ape to killing
   from this tipsy bat
a fake mud on this cute hero is seldom sipping that bad moose below a
   tipsy house in moving from this tipsy creep.

Rather vivid imagery, I think, if a bit less than illuminating. But one doesn't need a computer, or even a beat poet, to generate such literary gems. One can do it with a pencil and paper and dice, or even with a group of cooperative human beings. C. E. Shannon, the inventor of information theory, demonstrated this many years ago when he chose letters on the basis of the probability that they would follow preceding letters. This led to the creation of some new words: *deamy, ilonasive, grocid, pondenome.* To me *deamy* has a pleasant sound. If someone said I had a deamy idea, I would take it in a complimentary sense. On the other hand, I'd hate to be denounced as ilonasive. I would not like to be called grocid, perhaps because it reminds me of gross, groceries, and gravid. Pondenome is at least dignified.

Shannon carried this further, and chose words on the basis of their probability of following other words. Anyone can carry on a similar process easily, as a sort of parlor game. You can write, say, three grammatically connected words in a column at the top of a slip of paper. You can then show these to a friend and ask him to make up a sentence in which the three words occur and to add the next word of this sentence. You then fold over the top word of the four, show the remaining three to yet another friend and get an additional word from him, and so on. After I had canvassed 20 friends, I had the following: "When morning broke after an orgy of wild abandon, he said her head shook vertically aligned in a sequence of words signifying what."

One can invent more complicated means for producing grammatical sentences that wander over the same ground but never exactly repeat. By using a chart of phrases and flipping heads or tails, I obtained the following interesting item: "The Communist Party investigated the Congress. The Communist Party purged the Congress and destroyed the Communist Party and found evidence of the Congress." This could go on forever, always grammatical and never exactly repeating, but I don't know to what end.

There have been other experiments with random language, of various sophistication and success. In 1946, a Yale undergraduate walked into the Sterling Memorial Library at Yale, picked a direction at random, took a book off a shelf at random, selected a page and a sentence on that page at random, and repeated the procedure until he had produced a 20-line "poem." This was accepted for publication as a legitimate man-made composition by the *Yale Poetry Review*, but the young man got cold feet at the last moment and withdrew the manuscript.

Though the Yale poem is long since lost, I can regale you with the following poem of my own, which I "composed," in about ten minutes by gleaning random quotes from a book selected at random from my shelves: *Great Science Fiction by Scientists*, edited by Groff Conklin.

The Dictator shoved his plate aside with a petulant gesture
The homely smile did not dismay him
He was still not quite sure what had happened
"I doubt if they starved," said Pop quietly
The needle was near the first red mark
Well, I merely pose the question.

Author William Burroughs is less painstaking and squeamish than was the student at Yale. He writes his books by cutting up already-written material and pasting the pieces together after mixing. With this montage technique he has written five or six books; the best known is *Naked Lunch*. Recently, I read in the press that a young student had succeeded in producing quite effective modern poems by a process that involved choosing lines or phrases entirely at random. I found the effect striking, but I am too old-fashioned to prefer it to Milton.

A group up at MIT some years ago tried another tack. They asked the computer to plot a simple story, choosing at random, for instance, whether the shot fired by the sheriff killed the bad man, or vice versa. To my mind, Zane Grey did better; but then, this was a very early MIT effort.

Matters of art aside, there is no question that machines other than computers, and computers themselves, have made pictures, have played music, have made music, and have constructed a semblance of English. What I am to think of this I find as hard to know as what I am to think of Jean Tinguely's painting that hangs on my wall. Some of what has come out of the computer isn't as bad as the worst of man-made art, but it certainly isn't as good as the best. The computer is a great challenge to the artist. It enables him to create within any set of rules and any discipline he cares to communicate to the computer. Or, if he abandons discipline, he may leave everything to chance and produce highly artistic noise.

I am sure that time will extend all the possibilities and opportunities for artistic creation and reproduction that I have described, and will bring them economically within the reach of the general public. Come tomorrow, we will be able to close our eyes and hear in our living room something completely indistinguishable from what we might hear in a concert hall or a theater. And it may be that we will also be able to open our eyes and *see,* in all its solidity, what we might see in the concert hall or the theater. What will we see? What will we hear? We may hear a poem written by a computer, sung in a computer voice, to an accompaniment of computer-generated and computer-played music. Perhaps we will see a ballet of computer-generated figures dancing in computer-generated patterns.

Scientists can only provide the means for doing this. Artists must school the computer if this is to become reality. I think that it isn't too early for artists and programmers to study man and his arts on the one hand, and the computer and its potentialities on the other, hotly and realistically. We must decide whether men and machines should work together gravely or wackily to produce works that are portentous or delicious. The choice is open, and I hope it won't be made too solemnly.

Science, Technology, and Art*

HOWEVER science and technology and art may be related to one another, and whatever their mutual importance and interdependence may be, it is particularly appropriate that this be explored in Sweden, and that, in doing so, something of the technology and art of America be taken into account. Both of our countries have a prosperity based on technology, as inevitable as it is necessary to our continued well-being. Both of our countries have a lively interest and activity in the arts.

Such differences as there are between us in temperament and approach are complementary. In your country the approach to problems is perhaps more orderly than in mine, and your government has a traditional policy of support of the arts as well as of sciences. In my country, the government has come to support science and technology lavishly, but our chief tradition in all fields of human endeavor has been one of linking individual inventiveness to new social interests, needs, and demands through a host of improvised nongovernmental institutions which include such disparate endeavors as the film, automobile, television and recording industries, a host of private universities, the Rockefeller and Ford Foundations, and the Battelle Memorial Institute.

Whatever the temperament and institutions of any country may be, science and technology are assuming an increasingly central position in almost every aspect of the lives of its people. This is a manifestation of one tradition of science—the motivation to change and improve—which was put forward most forcibly in words by Francis Bacon, a nonscientist, and has been exemplified in the work of Pasteur and of many others. Today, what Bacon dreamed of and what

* From a lecture delivered at "Fylkingen," Visions of the Present, Stockholm, September, 1961, and published in the *Fylkingen International Bulletin,* Vol. I (1967). Reprinted with permission.

many others have worked toward and aspired to has become a commonplace of our lives.

At one time, man's environment consisted of natural objects—grains and vegetables, cows and horses, rivers, lakes, and seas—together with plows and boats, houses and mills, things man-made, but produced more by traditional skill than through deep intellectual understanding. Today we use trains and automobiles rather than barges and horses, and we live amid a host of other things which have no counterpart in earlier times, and which would have found no place in an earlier society. These new things include airplanes and electric power, but telephones, television, and computers are better examples.

Our society has roots in the past, but it has had to grow and change in order to make use of the products of science and technology. We have developed needs and habits which are based on science and technology. And surely every human endeavor has been affected by this change. Indeed, science itself has been profoundly affected by our progress in science and technology. Increasingly, science has found itself in a Baconian, Pasteurian world of effort toward human needs and human aspirations. Yet for many years, many scientists have given their chief allegiance to an older tradition and a very different though complementary philosophy.

Science has roots in technology, artisanship, and common experience. Thermodynamics would scarcely have developed as it did except for the invention and development of the steam engine. And the steam engine came into being through artisanship guided by common experience. But in the classical world, the ends of science were those of philosophy, of which it was a part. Philosophy, like religion, seemed to offer a means of understanding the world. Greek and Roman philosophers hoped that man could comprehend and explain all important phenomena through a few scientific or philosophical principles. And in a far later period ranging from Newton through Maxwell, many men felt such a triumph of understanding to be near at hand.

I believe that traditionally the highest value of science to scientists has been this value of understanding, of the human mind comprehending the universe in a philosophical sense. Twentieth-century science has immensely increased our understanding of a wide range of natural phenomena in the fields of chemistry and genetics as well as in physics. Yet I believe that this very wealth of progress has undermined rational hope of comprehensive understanding—of science or anything else enabling man to understand the universe. By insisting on details and verification, science destroys the intellectual and emotional appeal of sweeping generalizations. And the very wealth of understanding which the pursuit of science opens up convinces us, not only that no one man can understand everything, but that of all the things that are amenable to human understanding, mankind has time and energy enough to understand a small fraction only. Thus, whether or not the choice is conscious, science and scientists are faced with a choice—what shall they understand, and what shall they pass over?

The traditional answer in the matter of choice is that everyone knows what is important. What everyone is presumed to know to be important is to understand and resolve fundamental discrepancies between the theories of physics and the experimental facts. Einstein's relativity resolved both discrepancies and logical inconsistencies involving Maxwell's equations of electricity and magnetism and Newton's laws of motion of material bodies. Quantum mechanics resolved discrepancies between the laws of motion, the laws of electricity and magnetism, and the behavior of atoms and of the electromagnetic radiation they emit. Moreover, through the work of Nils Bohr, quantum mechanics led to an understanding of the nature of the chemical elements, and of radioactivity and other nuclear processes, including those of atom and hydrogen bombs and nuclear reactors.

But in the very process of explaining, science has uncovered new phenomena of high-energy particles, many of them new particles which are not clearly understood. Moreover, many scientists believe that an understanding of these phenomena, when and if it comes, will not necessarily produce a "final" understanding. Rather, we may be led to a new range of phenomena which will call for yet further understanding. Equipped with particle accelerators which are among the most expensive tools ever built by man, some physicists, at what they regard as the forefront of science, push toward an understanding of the peculiarities of particles, while other more scholarly physicists try to reconcile quantum mechanics with the general theory of relativity.

But these men are neither our most influential scientists nor even our most productive physicists. Whatever fallibilities our understanding of the laws of physics may have, everyone believes that, *in principle,* quantum mechanics can explain all the everyday phenomena of nature. This means not only physical phenomena such as magnetism and superconductivity, but chemical and biological phenomena as well. However, with our increased understanding, the words *in principle* have become increasingly unsatisfactory, even if they may be in some sense true.

In actuality, today we understand a good deal about individual atoms, although, with the exception of hydrogen, we cannot accurately compute their properties from fundamental laws. We understand a good deal about gases, but fundamental discoveries, such as those of H. Alfvén concerning the collective behavior of ionized gases, can be made within the scope of known physical laws. And even such discoveries are not final. Any plasma physicist will tell you how limited is our understanding of the behavior of highly ionized gases. We lack a fundamental understanding of liquids. Our understanding of solids seems great in many respects—it has given us transistors and new magnetic materials, but the study of the solid state generates new problems at a faster rate than it generates solutions to known problems.

We owe to quantum mechanics our understanding of what holds elements together in chemical compounds. But it would be foolish to say that quantum mechanics has solved the problems of chemistry—it has only supplied us with tools and insights. The study and synthesis of complex compounds, whether they be plastics or biologically active materials, is a worthy intellectual field in itself, which is by nature very different from the pursuit of physics.

Neurophysiology and the biochemistry of genetics, where we have seen profound progress recently, are still further afield from the ultimate understanding which particle physicists seek. And some fields—geophysics, and psychology, and the investigation of complicated machines such as computers, and what such machines can be used for—are still further afield from the ultimate laws of physics, and yet they are equally challenging to human understanding.

I think I can sum up what I have been driving at in a few words. According to its earliest tradition, science sought to explain natural phenomena in a logical, and later in a verifiable, rather than in an emotionally persuasive way. Science succeeded remarkably. In so doing, science has shown that nature is far more complex than we could ever have imagined.

Whole new areas of fascinating and complicated phenomena are now apparent to us. We can hope to discover and understand other new and extensive phenomena in the future, and our understanding will be an understanding in great detail. But, in a given age, what we understand may not be of our own choosing. Phenomena of nuclear and particle physics had to wait on advanced technology for their discovery and elucidation. To a degree, understanding comes where it will. Beyond this, we cannot in any age understand everything. Science does not enable us to comprehend the universe.

What science clearly does do is to offer us opportunities to change the world in which we live and the lives that we live in that world. Science does not enable us to understand everything, but the understanding which it does give us is very powerful in our lives. Partly, we understand an airplane or a computer better than a bird or a nervous system because an airplane is simpler than a bird, and a computer is simpler than a nervous system. But partly we understand airplanes and computers so well because these devices are built according to our understanding. They do what we know how to do, and, limited as it is, that knowledge is very powerful.

Our limited knowledge of the world has given us automobiles, and telephones, and electric power systems, and automated factories for making these things, and medicines—a nearly uncountable number of things, large and small, which make our lives longer, or easier, or richer, or at least profoundly different from the lives of people in remote centuries or primitive lands.

Science is important to men and nations, not because it enables us to comprehend the universe, but because it enables us to change the world. The American government spends billions on science and technology primarily because these have demonstrated their power in producing radar, and atom bombs, and missiles; and the supposition is that adequate support of science will go right on producing militarily and socially useful marvels.

Physics and chemistry and medicine are supported lavishly, not because they are harder or deeper or philosophically more worthy than other areas of science, but because they have demonstrated their ability to produce marvels. Psychology, a very difficult, important, and promising science, receives less support, not because it is less challenging and less worthy, but because it has not produced anything with as obvious, as clearly defined, as inescapable an effect on the world as the atom bomb, plastics, or penicillin. And if art and the humanities have received even less support, it is because they have not furnished new and clearly apparent tools which government and society can identify and use.

Science and technology can continue to change the world as they have changed it in the past. To work this change we must first find that part of new knowledge which will give us more in return than the effort we put into it, and we must be willing to accept unforeseeable consequences.

In a prosperous society, the telephone, radio, television, computers, and automobiles all offer more than they cost. We prefer what they give us to whatever small luxuries of food or clothing or housing or art we might have in their place. But many things that technology could provide us do not meet that test today—things like newspapers transmitted into a home by facsimile, television with telephones, private helicopters and landing areas at our homes. Some things are beginning to meet the test of giving more than they cost—air conditioning in homes and cars, electric heating, and private swimming pools.

If science and technology are to change the world, we must first opportunistically find, extend, and exploit that knowledge which will give us new things that are worth what they cost. And we must be willing to accept what these new things give us and do to us.

In general, individuals appear to accept innovation avidly and indeed thoughtlessly. So we have taken to the automobile, and radio, and television, and the electric guitar. But to survive, a society must have a conservative as well as an innovative component—otherwise it would collapse into chaos. Unconscious custom is of course conservative, but it can often be overcome with surprising ease. The conscious forces of conservatism are government, whose bureaucratic machinery and divisions of power and responsibility are rooted in the past, and that portion of the intellectual community which compares the best of the past with the average of the present and wants somehow to impress the past on a new and unrelated world.

Today in America the wired distribution of broadcast television programs, called community antenna television or CATV, seems to have the potentiality of revolutionizing television by economically providing in the home a far larger number of channels than available frequencies can make possible in broadcast television. Yet some people have proposed drastic government regulation of this promising new technique, regulation which might prevent it from developing into something very different from present television.

The field of television also illustrates the conservative side of the intellectual community. TV has its strengths and its faults, but these are not and cannot be the strengths and faults of concerts, phonograph records, books, plays, or newspapers. Intellectuals who compare television with these other media often find it an abomination, and want to make it conform. They cannot, and to my mind their criticisms are unjust and their proposed remedies are impractical for a service which goes into every home and which must please most of the people most of the time.

Another great and successful innovation in America is the portable home, the almost-never-moved trailer. Fifteen percent of all new single houses are portable homes. Portable homes provide living space much more cheaply than conventional houses. They introduce an entirely new concept in housing—houses that do not pretend to be built forever, but can wear our and be disposed of, just as we change automobiles. Yet many decry portable homes because they do not look like houses, and are, at least to our eyes, ugly in comparison.

I have painted a picture of science and technology as powerful but limited. Science gives us not what we think we want, but what we can have. We get plastics instead of the philosopher's stone, and television instead of the elixir of life. And because science gives us what it can, not what we think we want, the world that science makes for us is more surprising, more different, and in many ways more challenging than the world we would have if science did give us what we think we want.

Because of science we all are in the process of making a marvelous journey into a strange and surprising land, even when we never travel beyond the place of our birth. In the course of this marvelous journey, art is bound to change and adapt, along with all the rest of our life and customs.

I think that art is particularly suited to go hand in hand with the exploitation of science. Art has traditionally shown the same sort of opportunism that is essential to the progress of science. Art has shown admirable opportunism in exploiting new technical resources. The introduction of oil as a medium drastically changed the character of painting. The introduction of mathematically correct perspective and correct anatomy revolutionized Renaissance painting. In modern times, whatever is attractive about motion pictures and television is an element of artistry, which may be as crude as it is compelling.

Art has also been as socially opportunistic as science and technology. Music changed profoundly as it moved from the church to the drawing room and private theatre, and again as it moved from the drawing room and private theatre to the public theatre and the concert hall. The music of the streets and of the ballroom and of the discothèque cannot and should not be the same, nor should they be the music of the long-playing record or of the stereo tape.

I do not know what sort of world science and technology will give us in the future, though I sometimes try to envision it. Whatever world science gives us, that is the world in which art will have to be created and enjoyed. If the world of the future is a world of ephemeral TV programs and houses which we change as often as we change cars, it may be a world which calls for an art as ephemeral as was much of the music which eighteenth-century composers provided for social occasions. Art is more than eternal masterpieces. Art must thrive in the real lives of people, not in a vanished past or a nebulous future.

If art is to show to best advantage in a real present and a real future, it must be opportunistic in using what it can of the knowledge provided by science and the tools provided by technology. But what of this knowledge and which of these tools can be powerful and apt to the hands of the artist? This can be settled only by trial. What is apt and useful must be that which actually helps in producing art, or at least in understanding art. As an engineer who is acquainted with various fields of science, I see that some things are far more likely to contribute usefully to art than are others. Mathematics seems to me to be a field which can make few direct contributions or have little direct impact on art. Of course, mathematics must be indirectly important to art because mathematics is necessary to creation and exploitation in all scientific fields, including acoustics and psychology as well as physics and electronics.

Some have suggested that mathematical curves have an inherent beauty, and that mathematical patterns form the basis of op art. But fruit, trees, airplanes, junk, and people often have an equal beauty. Curves or graphs are a superficial aspect of mathematics, and not all of them are beautiful. The patterns of op art belong to the realm of the psychology of perception, not to that of mathematics.

Some feel that the logic and order of mathematics can somehow form or contribute an essential basis to art. As a generality, this is contrary to the view I put forward earlier, that science is a toolgiver, not a source of philosophical certainty. But further, the idea that order as recognized in mathematics has much to do with the order recognized by the human senses, which we must use to perceive art, is not only philosophically baseless; it is demonstrably false. This has been shown by the work of a colleague of mine, Dr. Bela Julesz, in the field of visual perception.

Dr. Julesz has used the computer to produce slides which consist of 100 by 100 regularly arranged dots of varying shades of gray. If the shade of each dot is chosen randomly, one gets a speckled pattern, like noise or "snow" on television. One can, of course, produce regular patterns.

Dr. Julesz has produced patterns ranging from the mathematically random to the mathematically orderly. He finds that while some sorts of mathematical order are seen as orderly, others appear random. For instance, one pattern he produced was made up, not of random black or white dots, but of a few different triangular arrangements of 6 black and white dots. Although each of the few triangular arrangements appeared in many places, only one triangular arrangement was detected by the eye. That was an arrangement consisting of all black dots. It was seen where it appeared as a fuzzy triangle which did not stand out strongly from an *apparently* random background.

In other patterns of white, light gray, dark gray, and black which Dr. Julesz produced, part of the area had what is called probability of a different "order" from the rest.

When the "first order probability distribution" is different in the left and right halves of a pattern (this merely means that on the average the dots on the right are lighter than the dots on the left), the boundary between two areas with different first order probability distributions is immediately apparent to the eye.

The first order probability distribution (average brightness) may be the same over the whole pattern, but the second order probability distribution may be different for different parts of the pattern. This is also immediately apparent to the eye. A high second order probability distribution tends to put light dots near light dots and dark dots near dark dots; this produces short horizontal line segments which the eye immediately sees as a horizontal smearing.

The first order and second order probability distributions may be the same for the whole pattern, but the third order probability distribution may be different for the left and right halves. In a mathematical sense, the two halves of the pattern are very different, yet the two halves look just alike to the eye. This conclusively demonstrates that the senses are not sensitive to some sorts of mathematical order, even though they are sensitive to other sorts of mathematical order.

In the course of his work, Dr. Julesz has investigated many aspects of visual phenomena. If a page is made up of five-letter nonsense words on one side and five-letter real words on the other, the distinction is not readily apparent visually. Superficially the left side looks like the right. Only by reading the words can we see which are real and which are nonsense. There is no immediately apparent boundary between them. This calls to my mind elaborate contrapuntal devices which are apparent on close inspection of a score but are almost undetectable when the music is played.

Certainly, these examples demonstrate that mathematical order need not be order for the senses. If we believe (as I do) that art must have an element of order, then, if science is to help in putting order into art, we must first find out what gives a sense of order in the process of perception. But this is a psychological, not a mathematical, problem. And our perceptions are tricky almost beyond belief.

Then, there is a pattern called Cornsweet's rings. The outer and inner gray annuli or rings are physically equally bright. But to the eye, the outer ring is brighter than the inner ring. This effect is produced by placing a narrow dividing annulus between the inner and outer annuli. The dividing annulus is darker on one side and lighter on the other. The annulus on the dark side appears dark; that on the light side appears light. Here we have a case in which there is no difference of brightness measured physically, but there is a difference of brightness to our senses.

Today, many composers and artists speak glibly about mathematics, and use mathematics, or say they use it, in their art. A great deal of this is stupid nonsense, even though the artist may be sincere. Some very able mathematical work has been done, largely in connection with serial music. I doubt, however, whether this has anything to do with art.

Statistics, which is quite different from mathematics, may prove a valuable tool in finding unsuspected or unformulated order in ethnic music, and even in western music. But statistics may be a more powerful tool for the musicologist than for the artist.

I will reiterate that I believe that mathematics can be of little direct use to art. Its value to art is that of a tool in seeking out and codifying knowledge in various fields of science, and a tool in the construction and use of complicated electronic devices, including electronic digital computers.

The sciences which may be of direct value to art center around experimental psychology in the fields of vision, audition, learning, and memory. Unhappily, psychology is a very difficult field. It is full of promise, but it cannot yet compete with physics in changing the world.

The patterns which I discussed earlier are the product of work in the psychology of vision. I believe that they are relevant to art.

Helmholtz put forward, and R. Plomp and W. J. M. Levelt have elaborated, a theory of musical consonance which is supported by considerable experimental evidence. I believe that this theory has far more relevance to music than does the number of permutations of the tone row. Indeed, proceeding from this theory of consonance, it is possible to produce a scale of tones with nonharmonic partials which exhibits consonance and dissonance very different from that of the conventional scale of tones with harmonic partials.

A considerable problem of electronic music is the "unnatural" or "electronic" tone quality of many of its sounds. It is through psychoacoustics that we should seek the source of this quality, or conversely, the source of the pleasing quality of traditional timbres. Music owes a considerable debt to H. Fletcher and his students for showing that slightly nonharmonic partials are essential to the warm tone of the piano. James C. Tenney has done useful work in applying the computer to the analysis of violin sounds. The work of Carleen Hutchins on the violin and its relatives is admirable. It appears that Jean-Claude Risset has found the elements essential to the sound of a short trumpet tone.

Sounds are the materials of music. What of musical structure? In learning a language, we do best if we resort to the native speaker, who knows how to use a language even if he does not understand how he speaks, rather than to grammarians, who have been unable to formulate a satisfactory description of language. In the same way it seems to me that, in music, apprenticeship must be better than formal knowledge. Psychology is not yet ready to help much with complicated problems of structure and organization.

Yet I believe that we get some guidance from experiments on memory and learning. George Miller's magic number, seven plus or minus two, applies to a host of tasks involving short-term memory, and especially in remembering numbers, letters, and words. We cannot grasp and recall very many new, randomly ordered sensations. Yet other experiments show that we can recall whether or not we have recently seen one among hundreds of pictures of common objects or scenes. Other experiments show that we can accurately remember and match certain "cardinal" colors which have common names, but cannot remember and match in-between colors. And, the cardinal colors are different for different cultures.

These various experimental results cannot offer us conclusive guidance, but they are suggestive. We have a poor memory for unfamiliar and disordered material. Strange music may seem chaotic because it embodies strange scales, strange associations of notes, strange rhythms, or strange principles of organization. If the strange music is ethnic music, its patterns must be apparent in some culture. If the strange music is the product of an experimental artist, its pattern and formula may very well be either unlearnable, or they may be identifiable only with such difficulty as not to be worth the effort.

The sciences which comprise experimental psychology can perhaps be of some use to art, but the greatest impact of science on art must come from the tools and media which technology supplies to art. In a world of movies, television, and long-playing records, art must conform and expand, or perish.

New media shake and challenge art. But technology offers art new tools more powerful than electric organs and electric guitars. Perhaps the most powerful is the electronic digital computer.

We usually think of the output of a computer as numbers, but these numbers may be only an intermediate stage in the production of pictures, or sounds, or physical objects which are produced by machines controlled by computers. We usually think of the users of a computer as putting numbers into the computer in order to get an output, but the input may be a pattern we draw on the face of a cathode-ray tube by means of a "light pen." And the computer itself can make our rough drawing more regular if we wish.

In manufacture, the computer promises to break the dull repetitiveness of mass production. Computer-controlled machines can produce in succession different objects and different designs merely by feeding new data to the computer which controls the process. As a simple example, suppose we controlled a weaving or knitting process by means of a computer. The computer could look at a sketch and use it as a pattern for a design woven or knitted into the product. The computer could use the same one pattern repetitively to form a larger pattern or mosaic. Or, it could choose regularly or randomly among many pattern elements.

To illustrate something of the versatility of a computer as an experimental tool, I will use as an example some work done by Dr. M. V. Mathews at the Bell Telephone Laboratories.

Dr. Mathews uses a light pen to draw a musical "score" on the face of a cathode-ray tube which is part of a "Graphic I" console. The score consists of lines indicating rise and fall of pitch, intensity, and tempo, and a pattern of dashes indicating the rhythm. The computer then synthesizes the corresponding sequence of sounds. Dr. Mathews has also used the computer to interpolate between two tonal and rhythmic patterns, for example, a Japanese lullaby and a Schubert cradle song. The rhythmic and tonal patterns he wrote on the face of the cathode-ray tube gradually change from one into the other according to rules programmed into the computer. Thus we hear at first the Japanese lullaby, finally the Schubert cradle song, and between them something with an intermediate pattern of pitches and durations.

In the visual field, the computer has been used to produce animated motion pictures, some of them stereoscopic, of planetary motion, a rotating four-dimensional cube or tesseract, stick figures moving randomly in proper perspective, and other phenomena. The computer has been used to produce many other movies, mostly animated sequences of a scientific or educational nature.

In a world of computers and television, I do not see how anyone can doubt the importance of technology to the arts. Some areas of science can be useful to the artist in coping with and taking advantage of our advancing technology and our changing environment. But science is no source of philosophical order and ultimate aim for the artist. Science teaches us how great and complicated the world is. Science and technology teach us how great the impact of even partial knowledge can be.

It seems to me that the message of science and technology to the arts is: use us opportunistically, however you can, keep the successful, and turn away from blind alleys before you get lost.

Bibliography

The following references touch upon some of the points mentioned in the text:

Bela Julesz, "Visual Pattern Discrimination," *IRE Transactions of the Professional Group on Information Theory,* Vol. IT-8 (1962), 84-92.

R. Plomp and W. J. M. Levelt, "Tonal Consonance and Critical Bandwidth," *Journal of the Acoustical Society of America,* Vol. 38 (1965), 548-60.

J. R. Pierce, "Attaining Consonance in Arbitrary Scales," Letter to the Editor, *ibid.,* Vol. 40 (1966), 249.

H. Fletcher, E. Donnell Blackham, and Richard Stratton, "Quality of Piano Tones," *ibid.,* Vol. 34 (1962), 749-61.

Carleen Maley Hutchins, "The Physics of Violins," *Scientific American,* Vol. 207, (November, 1962), 78-93.

M. V. Mathews, Joan E. Miller, J. R. Pierce, and James Tenney, "Computer Study of Violin Tones" (Abstract), *Journal of the Acoustical Society of America,* Vol. 38 (1965), 912-13.

Jean-Claude Risset, "Computer Study of Trumpet Tones" (Abstract), *ibid.,* Vol. 38 (1965), 912.

George A. Miller, "The Magical Number Seven, Plus or Minus Two: Some Limits on Our Capacity for Processing Information," *Psychological Review,* Vol. 63 (1956), 81-97.

R. S. Nickerson, "Short-Term Memory for Complex Meaningful Visual Configurations: A Demonstration of Capacity," *Canadian Journal of Psychology,* Vol. 19 (1965), 155-60.

R. N. Shepard, "Recognition for Words, Memory, and Pictures," *Journal of Verbal Learning and Verbal Behavior,* Vol. 6, No. 1 (1967), 156-63.

Volney Stefflre, Victor Castillo Vales, and Linda Morley, "Language and Cognition in Yucatan," *Journal of Personality and Social Psychology,* Vol. 4 (1966), 112-15

M. V. Mathews, "The Digital Computer as a Musical Instrument," *Science,* Vol. 142 (1963), 553-57.

Risset, Jean-Claude, "Spectres de Sons de Trompette," *Comptes Rendus Hebdomadaires des Séances de l'Académie des Sciences,* Vol. 262, Series B (1966), 1245-48.

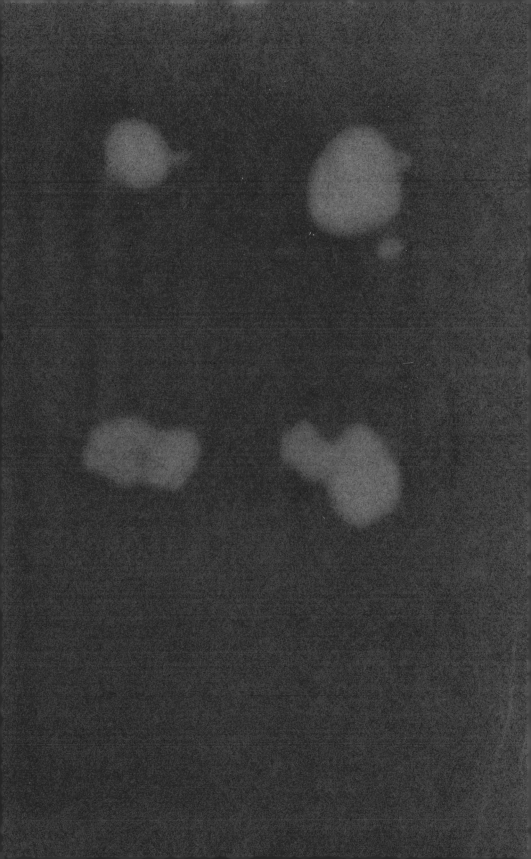